GOD

CREATED

WOMAN

ALIKE HERSELF

ZIRAH ALAIN

Ordering Information:

Prime Seven Media
518 Landmann St.
Tomah City, WI 54660

Printed in the United States of America

Books by the same author

Strass & Paillettes – Le journal d'un festivalier,
(AZ Productions, Marseille, 2011)

Dieu a créé la femme à son image,
(Éditions Thierry Sajat, Paris, 2014)

Du sang sur le tapis rouge – Kat Ladies,
(Prix Art Freedom 2016 - Éditions Thierry Sajat, Paris)

Rock Fictions (1976-2016),
(Société des Écrivains, Paris, 2017)

Dans les coulisses du festival de Cannes
(Société des Écrivains, Paris, 2017)

Interdit aux Hommes
(La Librairie Numérique de Monaco, 2018)

Cannes Backstage - Dans les coulisses du festival
(Nombre7, Paris, 2023)

Dieu a créé la femme à son image,
(Éditions Thierry Sajat, Paris, 2023)

***

Translation by Herve LECHEVALIER
Picture on the cover by Alain ZIRAH

© AlainZirah

This book is dedicated to all the women who have been important in my life. This book is therefore dedicated to Lucy, the first woman. God created woman alike herself. God is a woman. At the beginning, she was short and black.

First of all, I dedicate this book to Arlette, my mother, who has always supported me in my creativity and has transmitted to me her artistic fiber

To Ever, Nathalie and Fleur, with their heads in the stars, to Heylen and Sabrina, to Beatrice and Anna, the *"virtuoso knife"*.

To Mathy for her classy fashion style and the walks in Paris, to Solène LadyKat, my mischievous little cat, to Joëlle who gave life to my clone, to Elle who made me discover Santa Monica, to the beautiful Verane and her friendly smile, to Virginie, Rachel, Laurence and the tall Martine with her BB look.

To Isabelle who gave me the most beautiful gifts and brought love and suffering, to the beautiful Christine and my little black sister Kenny, to Yacine, my black- blooded RoussyKat.

To Faustine, my velvet whim of whom I am so proud.

To Anne Marie, my authentic princess from Casamance and companion of life with all my love.

And if God is a woman, I dedicate this book to her beautiful goddess legs.

I hope that everyone will find their way into these texts and I apologize to those I forget.

Women, I love you

Alain ZIRAH

PREAMBLE

It is generally said that God created man after his image,
That woman was created from the rib of the first man.
This machistic idea implies that man has a divine character,
That women are an inferior product after men.
This philosophy has belittled women in many countries
And almost every civilization for 6,000 years.

It is time to end this false theory.
God created woman alike herself.
Because God is a woman. And besides, she's black.
Her name is Lucy and she appeared in Africa in the Uomo Valley.
Or she is a brunette, named Lilith and has refused to submit to a man.
Or she's blonde with blue eyes, called Eve or Paris Hilton....
Or maybe she's Asian....

We're not going to rewrite history, but today, after Simone de
Beauvoir,
it takes a man and a book to reopen the debate and demonstrate that
women have always been superior to men.
These texts are a tribute to women by a man who loves women.
And puts them on a pedestal.

GOD CREATED WOMAN ALIKE HERSELF

LILITH, BLACK AND DOMINATRIX

By what strange spell, in Genesis (1-27 and 2-22) God decides to create humans in his own image, both male and female? God creates man and woman, two creatures back to back, from clay. Precisely he draws them from the clay of the earth. God is omnipresent and capable of everything. He is the ying and the yang, both male and female. When he brings his two creatures the breath of life, the gardens of Eden welcome two new characters to whom he has given the power to command the animals.

In some legends and in the Kabala, around - 2070 (we are in 5782!), after having spent six days to create the universe and all that is in it, God creates Adam and Lilith. Long before Eve. Contrary to popular imagery, Lilith is a beautiful dark-haired woman, probably even black. It is even claimed that the Queen of Sheba, black and Jewish, was a descendant of Lilith. In the same way as the wife of Moses, Tsippora the Kushite (Ethiopian) who was later called Sephora, like the perfume and cosmetics stores. We are far from the beautiful Venetian blonde painted by Sandro Botticelli in the Sistine Chapel.

It should be remembered that Lilith is mentioned in the book of Isaiah (34-14). This beautiful woman with black hair refuses to submit to Adam. What if she had followed all the 11,593 episodes of the soap opera The Young and the Restless available in 2021? Lilith is the first symbol of the feminist, black and dominating woman. I have often wondered how old Adam could have been when he was created. It took me years to discover in a book dedicated only to Genesis, in Hebrew and in French, the Sefer Bereshit (Book at the beginning), that Adam is created at the age of 20. This is obviously a symbolic age, and Lilith being drawn from the same loam as her benign Adam, I think she is the same age. After a period of living together where the beautiful brunette refuses to lie on her back under the only male inhabitant of the Garden of Eden and after having made him undergo her four wills (she is a woman!), she shows her man that she was created as a woman in the image of God. God also knows how to be a goddess.

After a number of years not defined by the texts, Adam, who dies at the age of 930 years (Genesis 5-5), decides to leave her and repudiates her, according to some. For others, it is Lilith who leaves her man to flee into the Red Sea. However, it was only men who transmitted the texts to each other, first verbally and then in manuscripts. So she is going to pass for a woman of bad life. Worse, and here you recognize yourselves, my faithful readers, the man who left her will call her a demon, a monster and a vampire.

Etymologically, Adam is the man from the clay and Lilith comes from the night. According to some Sumerian sources Lilith is the wind and the storm. She appears 3.000 years before J-C in the text of Gilgamesh in the Underworld, part of the Epic of Gilgamesh, a kind of hyper- muscular colossus who will give birth 5.000 years later to Hercules, then Tarzan and Conan, the barbarian. It is time to make a movie character out of him.

If the Hebrews, tyrannized by their Jewish mothers, have validated the concept of Lilith, it was not the same by the macho peoples of southern Europe. The Greeks will extend their civilization at the orders of Alexander the Great (born on July 21, 356 BC, died in Babylon on June 11, 323 BC). The scribes of the king of Macedonia will translate the texts from Hebrew. But there was no question for these dear macho phallocrats spending their time in the odors of sweat, blood, sweaty feet under the tents and fried food to accept that the first woman, their original mother, was a young black dominatrix who broke her lover's sweets and preferred to sit astride his stomach. She is therefore purely and simply deleted in the Greek translations of the Bible.

After the end of the Greek empire, Julius Caesar (born on July 13, 100 BC and died on March 15, 44 BC, in Rome), already emperor dominating his people but mistreated by his dominatrix Cleopatra, invaded the southern countries. His scribes translating the Bible into Latin from the Greek version will not have to worry about the existence or not of Lilith. It is even perfect for the Romans. Eve, blond and submissive, will be perfect to incite the soldiers to plunder the villages and rape all the female creatures that will pass within their reach. After the fall of Caesar assassinated by his own son Brutus comes the decline of the Roman Empire. But the writings remain. In Greek and Latin.

However, in the second century BC, the work written in Persian and entitled The Alphabet of Ben Sira presents Lilith as the first wife of Adam. As she does not get along with him, she flees into the Red Sea and refuses to return to the fold, despite the interventions of three angels, Sanoi, Sansenoi and Samengalof. Three doctor angels, protectors of men against demonic powers such as Samael, the dybbuk or the Golem.

In another Kabbalah tradition, Lilith and Samael are the two facets of a single androgynous creature, created in the image of God, back to back like the famous Janus. They hide under the throne of God and he, to punish them, separates them and projects them into the Garden of Eden. He condemns Lilith. She will not be able to have a child. The famous angels will authorize her to kill the children of men to eat them before their circumcision. After leaving Adam, Lilith finds her soul mate, Samael, marries him and settles with him in the valley of Jehanum or Gehenna. Samael becomes Belial and Lilith is represented as a femme fatale with wings or a mermaid's tail.

Both seductress and temptress, she is presented as gifted for incest, often very beautiful with long hair that she shines in all the mirrors of her palace and breasts to die for. But women still do not have a soul, until the Council of Thirty in 1530, and our male congeners have quickly, after a few years, to treat their companions of harpies, vampires, striges, Lorelei, Melusine, gorgons, Medusa, Scylla, mermaids, Sphinx, vouivres ... This is how women who refuse to submit to man are represented. Like Lilith. After being chased out of Eden, she is considered a demoness who seduces men while they sleep. If this speaks to you, it's because ideas have a hard skin in the brain of men.

Let's go back to our Garden of Eden and our lonely man spending his time running after goats, gazelles and other antelopes. After ten years of prayers and solicitations, around 2060 BC, Adam receives as a gift from heaven a beautiful, blonde, busty and submissive girl. Her name is Eve and she was drawn by God from one of his ribs. He has a perfect love affair with her and bangs her hard in the garden of delights.

But it can't be that idyllic! Women, sometimes you know how to be pests. It is already the case of Lilith. Chased out of Eden, she gets involved with Lucifer, the one who brings the light and finds her Samael. Animated by the firm intention to rot the life of her ex, she transforms herself into a tempting snake to incite the credulous bonde to bite into the forbidden fruit. The poor girl even feels obliged to offer the fruit to her Adam who is incapable of discernment. The story goes that both of them open their eyes and realize that they are naked. Eve becomes the first fashion designer by creating improbable clothes from vine leaves. God punishes his disobedient children appropriately and drives them out of the Garden of Eden.

Leaving a lush, bustling nature, Adam and Eve are forced to take refuge in caves to escape the wild beasts. Nine months later, the couple caresses the rounded belly of the sweat-soaked woman. They give birth to beautiful children, twins. In 2040 BC Cain was born with a twin sister named Luluwa. Etymologically, Cain means creator, javelin or craftsman. Luluwa means beautiful, because she was more beautiful than her mother. Depending on the source, she is sometimes called Lusia or Kalmana.

Adam and Eve don't have television and continue to spend hot days and evenings. It takes them another five years to have triplets Abel, and two sisters Awan and Aklia, in 2035 BC. Abel means breath and vanity. Adam forbids the boys to kiss their twin sister; but nothing is forbidden concerning the twin sister of the other. He decides that Abel will marry his brother's sister and Cain will marry Abel's sister. How can one produce offspring to populate the Earth if one does not sleep with the available women? There are very few of them at the beginning, except for their mother, and of course, this time does not know any taboo on incest. As a result, the three girls, Luluwa, Aklia and Awan, spend their time taking selfies and Snapchat to show off on Shabbat nights. Luluwa succeeds in all the beauty contests of the family. She is regularly designated as the most beautiful, at the expense of Awan.

Adam and Eve's two boys are a farmer, Cain, and a shepherd, Abel. Cain, the elder, plays Nicolas the gardener and produces fruit in his vegetable garden. On his side, Abel runs after the chickens. He discovers the taste of eggs, tries his hand at boletus omelets and hides behind the walls of his henhouse to see who comes first, the egg or the hen. He wants to question God who laughs at his offering of a basket of eggs on his first lamb. The creator prefers to delight in Abel's clusters of grapes as well as his peaches, figs and lychees. Disappointed, sad and full of anger, Cain finds himself ogling his sister Luluwa, Abel's twin. He makes advances to the beautiful one and decides to take her as a companion because he is the elder. Abel opposed it because she is his twin and they are fused. Year after year, Cain's jealousy and resentment towards his brother grows and grows. Cain is as jealous as a louse because he can't get off with chicks.

It must be said that life outside the Garden of Eden was not always easy. An authoritarian father Adam, a mother too nice to be honest, Eve, and lots of animals. The couple starts getting up at 4 am to come and milk the cows to get the good milk and run after the chickens. And not a single Karine Lemarchand to come and make them discover the love in the meadows! Very quickly, while his exhausted companion falls asleep, he starts to practice onanism and floods the green plants on the ground. Always on the lookout, Lilith, the mischievous one, comes to recover Adam's sperm on the ground, which she inseminates in the depths of her being. This allows her to give birth to swarms of demons. This adventure lasts more than 130 years.

With, fortunately, some incartades because the perverse brunette does not stop there. The story does not tell how she will seduce Abel, her own son-in-law, who came to visit her on the Red Sea. The 90 year old boy, who was still a virgin a few months earlier, is all excited to see the chocolate skinned beauty wiggling under his nose where the first hairs have grown. He wriggles like a roach when the beautiful black arsonist comes to squat on his belly to play Vampirella. Habits are quickly formed when it comes to food. The beautiful one knows how to fill the belly and the lower abdomen. She prefers to receive the seed of a young vigorous rather than to wait for her ex to come to recover it on the ground.

Cain is drunk with jealousy. The young nonagenarian of 95 years mounts a stratagem to be able, him also to have adventures with the beautiful African. Lilith takes pleasure in banging the two boys of her ex just to piss him off. She alternates evenings with Abel and with Cain and turns Cain against his brother. Unfortunately Cain will be surprised in full frolic by his brother. Abel threatens to tell everything on the social networks of the time, that is to say the father, the mother, the brother and the sisters. And eventually the many animals in the backyard that follow them. Their first followers.

*

\The years pass and Cain manages to marry his sister Luluwa. But for a short time. Luluwa hears Cain talking in his sleep and telling how he killed his brother. In a cave painting in his Cave of Treasures, Adam learns in the news feed that his son Cain murdered his son Abel, only a hundred years old. Disappointed, unhappy and mad with anger, Adam chases his son to distant lands, to the dry land. He takes with him a Luluwa devastated by grief and without the parents' agreement. Adam goes into grief mode and starts to pretend to have a headache when Eve approaches him. Their mourning will last one hundred and forty days.

Vexed to have let himself be trapped by his beautiful blonde, since the story of the apple, Adam pulls a six feet long head. He refuses to have any sexual relationship with Eve. But the blonde ends up convincing him that the planet must be populated. In a concern for the environment, Adam brings back his harebrained girlfriend to teach her the game of the beast with two backs. In 2030 BC, the couple quickly has a new litter of twins that they name Azura, the girl, and Seth, the boy. Maybe Eve had had two miscarriages? They were not very good at spelling and it was not until Ronsard that they compared the woman to a rose. Adam was already 230 years old, according to some texts. He has 700 years to live. And not a single new kid!

The years go by, inexorably (I remind you that Adam died at 930). As a young adult, Seth, as free as a bird, puts his berlingot in the drawer of his older sister Azura (or Aklia). A whole line of bells and whistles will come out of the drawer, starting with Enosh. They will have lots of children, boys and girls generating a proud lineage until Noah. Again, the story doesn't tell how this happened, but incest between brother and sister was not yet taboo and Seth lived 912 years.

Cain made advances to the beautiful Azura, but she refused him. When he is chased to the land of Nod, east of Eden, Cain ends up with his ugly sister Awan. But after many years, what must happen happens. Cain ends up going out one night with Awan. The brother and sister have a son Enoch. A hard worker, Cain begins to build a city to house his numerous descendants. The city will be called Enoch. Many of Cain's children refused to follow in the footsteps of their murderous father and became artists, poets and singers. The most illustrious descendant will be a certain Noah to whom God will ask to gather couples of animals in a wooden ark which will survive the flood and will find themselves stranded on Mount Ararat, in Armenia.

This is how all humanity descends from Noah and how we are all a little Armenians.

*

How to tell all the turpitudes and vicissitudes of the human race to children? The relationship between Adam and his first wife, Lilith, who refuses to submit and invents the first subversive positions of the Kama Sutra. The son-in-law Cain who comes to visit his mother-in-law in wolf's clothing with a basket full of jam, honey and unleavened bread.

The matrons had not yet enticed their julots with bags of flour to open bakeries before sunrise. Illustrated on the walls of a cave in the form of the cave paintings of an early comic strip, the young centenarian in red hooded jogging suits going to see his mother-in-law suddenly changed into a she-wolf will inspire the first budding artists to tell stories to frighten the children.

Impossible to tell about Adam and Lilith's sexual relationship, to even explain that she was cast out because she refused to submit. The #metoo movement has come and gone and today no girl would accept that a man could chase her away just because he wanted to place his big oily paws on a young girl's thigh. She immediately dials 119 on her latest smartphone. Then she contacts SOS Femmes. Telling the story of an ex-girlfriend's revenge to ruin the life of the first man is not very glamorous for a little girl who only dreams of Cinderella and Prince Charming. To explain that the first man could not be satisfied with only one woman during his 930 years is to put a wet finger between the thighs of an innocent thought. Adult life is so complicated.

How do you explain the creation of man and woman to three or four year olds? It's so much easier to make children dream by explaining that Adam was lonely in his big garden and that while he was sleeping God pulled a girl from one of his ribs. That they loved each other, had children, and populated the Earth on which we stand. An idyllic vision, to be sure, but so much easier. But you, my faithful readers, are not four years old and now you know.

NEW SENSATIONS

Beautiful stranger, object of my fantasies, I don't know if you exist or if I am dreaming.
I can hear the sound of your heels slamming in the cold stairs. Click... click... click... click...

When you arrive, lying on the ground, prostrated at the feet of superior beauty,
I will offer my body. You will walk on your flying carpet... walk... walk... walk...

I'll slip into your shoes and lick your toes, one by one, And drag my docile tongue under the soles of your feet. Lick... Lick... Lick... Lick...

You'll sit on the sofa. My face will serve as a footrest
For the Egyptian Queen. Your charming pet will massage them for you. Relax... relax... relax... relax

My mouth will become a shoe to your size To keep your feet warm. Don't forget to bring four chocolate breads. You'll trample one on my body.
And you'll lick all the traces of chocolate off my skin. Yummy... yummy... yummy... yummy...

Too sexy in your mini white dress, my beautiful arsonist, I'm going to dress up as a thong with a tongue inwards.
to occupy your nights and make you scream your happiness. Lick... lick... lick... lick...

My tongue will explore the inside of your belly to make you scream the language of pleasure. scream... scream... scream... scream...

My nose stuck in your thong, you'll call me Pinocchio And you'll make me lie to you.
Grow... grow... grow... grow...

You will discover a multitude of new sensations. More... more... more... more...

You'll put wild strawberries on your body
And I'll come and lie on top of you before I lick your body... red... red... red... red...

I'll slip some carrots into my jeans before I lie on top of you.
You'll stir at your own pace without knowing if you should marry a raw vegetable.
You will close your eyes and beg: keep the same movement, Don't move. Don't move. You're the one who'll keep control. Rub... rub... rub... rub... rub...

My horn of flesh will search the inside of your body, visit your cave And your cries will fill the space with a concerto for the neighbors: yes... yes... yes... yes.

You will claim my face between your smooth, well-kept thighs. My tongue will drive you crazy... again... oh yes... again...

And when exhausted with love, drunk with incendiary sensations, you will fall asleep
I'll slip across the bed and offer my hair to caress your body.

I will feel the dead weight of your buttocks on my body, your feet on my cheek,
I'll smell the good smell of mixed sweat after sex. Hume... hume... hume... hume...

With my five senses awake, I will listen to the slight snoring and the squealing skin
As my eyes fill with images of the happiness of the moment. Because I know that when I wake up, everything will start all over again with dripping champagne
From your breasts to my mouth, from my wand standing in your mouth...
slurp.... slurp... slurp... slurp...

I will use your natural cut to quench my thirst and make you scream again.
And, in the warmth of a beautiful summer afternoon, I will discover the new flavors
Fruits caught, for a few moments, between your thighs.
Taste... taste... taste... taste...

Before you start exploring every nook and cranny of your skin again.
I'm gonna drive you crazy and you're gonna make me scream...
We're gonna scream...
Together.

LIVING FULL SPEED

Life is short, but it is long.
Life is long, but it is short.
No time to read what humanity
Has bequeathed to us. As time goes by,
Lives follow each other. Succession of emotions.

What's the point of asking questions,
They were already without answers, in Plato's time.
Amethyst in the place of the heart,
Your smile haunts my eternity.

My eyes enjoy every summer
To be rinsed with sea water. The girls
On the beaches sweat with eroticism.
Unmentionable thoughts, insolent and beautiful
Wet the clitoris of my timorous cerebellum.

I live at two hundred per hour.
Everything goes too fast, in too little time.
I surf with a distraught soul
Towards well firm and depilated calves.

They dance their lives these pretty buttocks
High and distinguished to be distinguished.
The young carefree silhouettes
Hide their fantasies behind paper masks.

My artist's life creates moments at two hundred
Euros frozen in an instantaneous eternity.
Before, a work of art lasted a lifetime.
One scrolls the moments of the life of others. And we forget.

Life has become surreal. We collect plastic
To pollute the oceans and hide our mute faces.
Everyone complains, but continues to buy their shampoo.
In museums, the ultimate works are dethroned by anonymous people
Filling entire walls with street art in the image of the coronavirus.

The demonstrations are limited to two hundred
People announced in the televisions
When the crowds invade the streets. They are afraid.
We make them afraid. Divide and conquer. Napoleon of operetta
Does what he can in the face of telephone operators and laboratories.

Life has become uncontrollable. To write this text,
I had to leave a café that was closing at the moment of inspiration,
The waiters were setting up the tables in the second place
where chatterboxes wanted so much to know me.

Then I had to endure the vindictive cries of the talent scout.
We call it domestic scenes. It's moving.
I just need to be alone to write.
To express emotions when they arise.
Without being disturbed. So much the worse if I have to change my
life!

I will finish this text on a small round wooden table.
The inspiration has escaped. The idea is truncated.
A life for two without respect is not worthy of a solitary life.

YOUR FEET RESTING ON MY BOOKS

Love falls on our heads
By opening a door, without warning.
Life is built, night after night,
By dint of complicit moments.

Smiles are like cement
To reinforce the walls of a house.
Everything is new, everything is beautiful.
The new moments are magical.

Then comes the wear and tear, the disagreements, the lack of love.
Everything becomes a pretext for not being able to stand each other
anymore.
What game are you playing, Cupid of the supermarkets,
By sending murderous arrows to test emotions?

The end of love delivers us by closing a door.
I don't want to see her anymore. Yet she dances under my eyelids.
Sitting at the edge of my lips, she dances a pump
Smoking an eternal cigarette in my secret thoughts.

I have loved you. At first sight I knew it was you.
I love you every moment. Your feet resting on my books Travel in
imaginary countries.
I will always love you, because it is to life, to death.

And we don't want to die.

THE CRIES
OF LOVE

When love has fled, what is left?
Of all those nights of love, of all those cries of love?
When your apricot discovered a foreign language.

The door opened. Your sun dazzled me.
As soon as I saw you, I knew you would be
The woman with the big smile of a lifetime.

I never thought the door would close on you.
So suddenly! At my request.
I didn't know that love could be a struggle.

Since you left, I don't know where,
Every night my heart screams your name.
I couldn't bring joy to your smile.
It's only at the end that we know the whole story.

Every day you made the words love rhyme with always.
How can I forget the woman in love
Who, from our union, made a mythical couple?

Don't have too much pain to say goodbye to me.
The woman is the future of the man,
But what happens to man when she is gone?

When I see you, I become totally crazy.
But if I don't see you, I go crazy.
At night I lie, I rely on you.

Now that we're apart
Our love will become eternal,
Like Gainsbourg and BB, but also with Baby Jane.

ANONYMOUS SUPERSTARS

Anonymous superstars of our own lives, we go through an ephemeral existence, under the eyes of our children
Who do not understand the contempt or indifference of their fathers,
Uncles and aunts criticized in secret.
They have understood life better and are moving to foreign countries.

Jealousy, envy, incomprehension in front of their fear of existing!
To live is not to accumulate numbers for a miserable withdrawal card.
It is not about living crumbs of life, intermittently!
We make memories to contemplate for our old days
Accompanied by renowned artists who make us citizens of the world.

If you could see what they have become, my father,
My life as an artist is a mystery to them.
How can one frequent the palaces of the mind
Without triggering, every day, crises of jealousy?

President thinks he owes nothing to anyone, too much money to know faith.
He looks for an imaginary resemblance with his father.
The mother castrated in her talents, excessive in her forms
But always aware of the subtleties, of the slightest feelings about the substance.

His wife boasts that she did it all by herself, this school teacher.
His doudou, too proud, has lost all notion of humility. Ivory tower.
They deprive humanity of the talents of others who will go to the
end of the world.

This desire to make others feel good about themselves
You have forgotten it, my dear, in the vanity of your narrow feelings.
Is there still something that makes you enjoy, dear accountant of
feelings.

When you are in a restaurant with your chosen half, do you count
The value of each of her bites. A carrot and a turnip.

Some collect numbers to give a reason to their existence
When artists collect encounters and make their hearts grow.
The pleasure is always double, when it is shared.

MEGALO DREAM

I write every day to give birth to my soul.
My raw words violate the virginity of the paper
And the power of the Word speeds up ideas.

Before, we were poets, today we write words.
To have chosen Total Art, it is a megalomaniac dream.
I did not choose between doing good or doing beautiful.

I leave a trace behind me to fuck the life.
I leave a trace behind me to fuck the life.

I like to make words shine, to suck emotions,
To make colors vibrate, to give new sensations.

Like a spider blinded by the light,
My iconography weaves a tentacular web.
I create monumental and collective works
On the television of the imaginary, tempting and inventive.

Before, we were poets, today we write words.
To have chosen Total Art, it is a megalomaniac dream.
I did not choose between doing good or doing beautiful.

I leave a trace behind me to fuck the life.
I leave a trace behind me to fuck the life.

I want to stay humble when greatness is an ego thing.
I would like to paint huge frescoes
To write a huge work like Les Misérables
That the elites will have stripped to the saddle.

Before, we were poets, today we write words.
To have chosen Total Art, it is a megalomaniac dream.
I did not choose between doing good or doing beautiful.

I leave a trace behind me to fuck the life.
I leave a trace behind me to fuck the life.

Before, we were poets, today we write words.
To have chosen Total Art, it is a megalomaniac dream.
I did not choose between doing good or doing beautiful.

I leave a trace behind me to fuck the life.
I leave a trace behind me to fuck the life.

DOMESTIC SCENES

I spent the whole night hating you
While insults and death threats rained down.
Too long I had waited for the warmth of your body.

How long, eyes riveted on a silent screen
Letting your old demon spill his bile, without respect?
And my ass, do you like my ass? It's in the movies.
The scenes of meningitis don't end up lying on a couch.

The faucet pours out reproaches and dark thoughts.
You wasted my time. I lost my youth.
All these sentences heard a thousand times, thoughtless.
When does youth begin and end, baby? I laugh.

I spent hours hating the evening delivery man,
responsible for all your woes, helping you drink
The memories of all you couldn't have.
Weak mind unable to overcome these moments of pain.
My only drug is you and you are my dealer.

The minutes pass, unperturbed, and also the hours.
You continue to pour out your streams of hatred, raw words,
frustrations.
We used to watch the hands of the clock
Waiting for the moments when you were praising me.

Embittered woman rehashes the past of a rainy life.
Prostrated, the man recognizes. He did not know how to make her
happy.
The words flow like incandescent lava.
He does not listen to her any more. She is too insolent.

What is the use of words now? We no longer communicate.
Shouting is so much easier. The old love is no more
Only a vague memory of good times shared.
Insults wake up consciences and call for a word in return.

I am the magnifying mirror of your feelings.
Love me and I make you a queen. Scream and I curse you.
The demon combs her long dead hair and takes out a breast from her
nightie.
She takes the pose in a disordered living room. He would like to love
her soul.

The numbed body wakes up his ardors. He tries a kind word.
The dragon is only a beautiful woman
Who waits to be reassured. That he takes her in his arms.

Then, like in a Spielberg movie,
The loathsome world of the slutty harpy
Has left the place to the decoration of the cuddly soul
Whose beauty leaves her no escape.

It is so easy to play with feelings.
To calm the angry man, a simulated fall
And here she is with sweet words that massage the sprained ankle.

Why, in love, the woman simulates and the man lies?

THIEF OF PRECIOUS MOMENTS

I have been seen at the foot of the Eiffel Tower
Charming shepherdesses with a lens.
I made love to forget my train.
I played dead, admired your rear end.

To make you more beautiful was my goal.
To make you more beautiful was my objective.

One saw me dragging my spats on the Old Port.
Making children to never be wrong.
Women have paraded in beautiful sheets.
The taste of their lips will never fade.

I was seen freezing moments on the red carpet,
Carrying artists, packing everything that moves
To illustrate a great album of glitter.
Yes, all these moments, they were so nice.

Making you more beautiful was my goal.
Making you more beautiful was my goal.

I was seen with Elle under the Hollywood letters
Celebrating Yom Kippur with Nathalie Wood's rav.
Globe-trotting from Los Angeles to San Francisco,
Took Steve's guitar and told me Toto.

I stole moments behind my dark glasses.
I stole moments, hung out in dark streets.

I was seen confined, under accumulated books,
Making videos. Walking in the streets, masked.
I found love again near a beach,
Scrolling images of happiness on pages.

I was seen to be ecstatic, at the top of Atlantis.
I swam in its waters of sulphur. Yellowed fabric, candid.
We were the masters of the world, in white and blue,
Towards sylphs and ruins, rode scooters like rookies.

To make you more beautiful was my goal.
To make you more beautiful was my goal.

I was seen on top of the World Trade Center
Comparing yellow cabs, under my feet, on the ground,
To insects. Between the wings of eagles, the snow on the towers
Fell on the Empire State, white and without detour.

In Morocco, I was seen dancing with snakes
To the sound of flutes, in a square with silver doors,
Picking up images in a park still asleep
Between tanners, water merchants and polygamy.

I stole moments behind my dark glasses.
I stole moments, hung out in dark streets.

To make you more beautiful was my goal.
To make you more beautiful was my goal.

INVITATION TO
THE CLOUDS

When love invites you to join the clouds,
You undress Cupid. The fool has no age.
You climb the ladder to happiness,
But leaves me at the bottom of the ladder, without any honor.

Sitting on the edge of my lips, you dance,
A cigarette at your fingertips, in a trance,
While I choose my evils,
The wooden bars pressed against my back.

Discovering your emotions on the tip of my tongue
Where you clean your most impure thoughts,
Raised on your heels, you come to seek refuge
While your toes lead me to the asylum.

Floating in the limb, crushed with happiness,
I keep an eye on your comings and goings.
All your body parts are offered, naked.
I'm reacting. I'm treacherous. In the blink of an eye, you kill me.

Your body expresses its passion for foreign languages
While in a strange way I repaint the shelves.
You're pulling me to the top, tigress,
And I come to fill you with ecstasy and tenderness.

With your legs raised to the sky, your body calls me.
You want something heavy. Attention, sweetheart,
I'm a safe box breaker, explorer,
Jackhammer of your thoughts, your worshiper.

Ivory slips over dark chocolate
And the images are accumulating in my memory.
Images of your body, dizziness of your heart,
Intense memories of moments of happiness.

I feel lighter and lighter, almost empty.
Your hands slap the air. I smile.
My fingers stuck against your butt, I survive
To your heel blows in the void.

You're looking for any cavity to house them.
You're the case from which I don't want to dislodge myself anymore.
We cannot derogate from the laws of embraces.
He did things right, our friend the clockmaker!

There comes a time when the man, who has become a sex toy,
Run the batteries of his sex appeal.
With authority, Mistress claims her boyfriend
To remind her that she remains a little girl.

The movements become even more precise.
Keep going! Don't stop... or I'll kill you!
I carry out the sentence with a smile on my face.
I like to look at my beautiful girl's eyes
When she comes.

The bodies intermingle again, in sweat.
The mouths fill with strong emotions.
The hand-to-hand combat has liberated everyone from all their fears.
And you stay smiling, motionless like a dead woman.

Your wet hair stuck against your cheek
Slip into my mouth.
My caliber between your legs is holding you at gunpoint.
But I collapse inside you and fall asleep like a stump.

Love is beautiful when feelings are shared
Because the pleasure is twofold when it is shared.

A WOMAN'S MAN FOR YOU

I looked at another girl, my treasure
And I told you about another love.
You blamed me; I was wrong.
It's you I want, sweetheart.

Of course, I'm only interested in girls, darling.
Blondes or redheads, tall or short,
Neither do brunettes, they don't count as plums.
Yet, through them, I only love you, my little fortune.

I like to watch the girls walking,
Their tanned legs marching,
Breasts that defy the laws of gravity,
Naughty eyes, a finger on seductive smiles...

And you're the one I place well elsewhere,
With your fair skin, with your chocolate skin.
You don't look like anyone, sweetheart.
So similar and so different. Unique, my sister.

Dare I compare you to that bold, racy Eurasian girl?
To the Japanese rascal? To that black beauty with ivory teeth,
Possessive and jealous... Just to see you there
Criticize the glossy girls lying on the glossy paper.

And there's you, that I place well elsewhere,
With your fair skin, with your chocolate skin.
You don't look like anyone, sweetheart.
So similar and so different. Unique, my sister.

LEICA PYGMALION

As soon as he wakes up, his ears filled with a music
that still has to be made,
I put on paper the stolen images of a film
that doesn't exist.
Where do they come, these fleeting illusions of a masked universe
Where girls are full of graces and dreams.

I get on my Leica like a Davidson Harley, go to the studio
And track down the glossy paper puppets with sweet words
To make them give birth to fantasies and fake love games.
Flashes and shots are my pen and paper.

Manufacturer of fantasies, I start my souvenirs factory
And forced my playmates to have solitary pleasures
Which will become mysteries, both so close and so far away.
One tears the prison from her breasts, the other shows off her
armadillo.

Plastic weapons are so effective on the soul
Magazine discoverers. And tears are more beautiful
When the ground blades fill your heart with tears...

AFRICA

I often believed that Love was your name
Yet you had a boy's first name.
We met. We loved each other. Then left. Served,
Was my soul! Your feet dance the rhythm of my life.

I wanted to bring you all my best, to become your teacher.
So, at the end of a chain, I offered you my heart.
Your mermaid body danced a long time on my eyelids.
My guitar strings were vibrating for you. So proud!

Look of embers, golden lips. Adored, my beautiful.
You were getting even more beautiful every day.
I drank your body every day until I was drunk.
And you spent all your time braiding your hair.

Your firm personality. I'm a real African!
My blood is black! Of course, you were a queen.
Your ebony skin called my tongue again and again...
I had become an alcoholic under your kisses and your body.

Look of embers, golden lips. Adored, my beautiful.
Believe it, you were getting even more beautiful every day.
I thought for a long time that with a golden chain, you'd be the one
Who, forever, would chain my rebellious soul...
Around your ankle, to dance with you to Africa.

And one day, love ran away, without any warning.
We take a break, we rest. We're casting off.
You don't know how to keep women!

I had been warned.
Grief and pain now leave my heart bare.
The little spark smothered the flame I loved
From that great fireworks display that will never glow again.
In the absence, the skins learn to peel off.

Look of embers, golden lips. Adored, my beautiful.
The memory of your skin calls out to my tongue, my female nigger.
I drank your naked body, indecent to the point of intoxication.
In the alcohol dance the memories of your cruel kisses!

Melancholy awakens memories of the dead kisses.
Your ebony skin set my cheeks on fire. Set me on fire.
Since then, in memory of your smile, I've been dancing, celebrating
So, I won't ever forget the one that's always dancing in my mind.

CHOCOLATE FINGERS

You can feel me inside,
You're thirsty for happiness.
I'm naked under your skin.
Your body is waving like a flag.

Sitting at the edge of my lips,
You give me some of your dreams.
My mouth makes your secrets dance.
Cambered, you stir your sweet skin.

In a previous life, I was used as a mattress.
Lying under your body, I'm staring at you right now,
You're bending your lower back,
And I massage your breasts.

Your belly button jealous of your feverish lips,
Shaken under my velvet tongue,
Thief's tongue, angel of value.
Under your eyelids, your eyes frown.

Your hand shows the way.
Your chocolate fingers are wriggling.
Your sensitive button welcomes my hand
While your taste buds tremble on your tongue.

Love is without appeal when the mouths merge.
Your belly dances as I pound it.
Saliva slips from the tender words into the hollow of the ear.
I hug you, you do the same.

You measure the comings and goings
From your lover inside your heart.
I take possession of your naked flesh
And offers life inside your body.

We accelerate the cadence, in silence in dance.
In my mouth, you come to find refuge
And the jerky movements, like under worming,
Freeze in a small death. Sublime and intense.

We kill ourselves with pleasure,
Happiness and communion of souls
Eager to start our lovemaking again,
Naked together, without any moods.

THE BEAUTIFUL
AND THE FLY

She is beautiful, very beautiful.
Savage and sweet, that's her.
Her mother is a real princess.
But she's an angel and a female devil.

She inherited this proud port
Of those for whom knights die.
As soon as she gets out of the bathtub,
On her bed, she spreads out her accessories.

She collects stiletto heels,
Mules and pumps, all the girl's shoes.
Her weapons for war against men are lipstick,
Make up and jewelry to generate fever.

She orders, smiles. Please...
How can we not satisfy all her wishes?
With her friends, Machistic Man shows off the beautiful one,
But with her, he becomes the fly from which she tears off the wings.

THE GIRL WHO ANSWERED WITH A SMILE

She is beautiful, very beautiful. She's savage and sweet.
Her mother is a real princess.
She inherited this proud port from well-born people.
She understood that in life, the main thing are accessories.

She collects high, very high heels.
Yet she is tall. And very fine.
You never could be too happy if you want to be a great lady.
When you know her, how can't you fall in love?

Quite often, when I glued my naked skin
Against her lower back, I was questioning her.
How do you see your future? Our future?
But the girl only answered... with a smile.

She dressed her friends like Barbie dolls.
Together, they would snap their heels
With sophisticated shapes on the dance floors, in summer.
And to male proposals, she only would respond... with a smile.

One evening, a man wanted to attack her.
But he immediately made him change his mind.
You are a God's child. Worse!
The weapons fell at the feet of the beautiful
And to urgent questions, she would only answer... with a smile.

AN ENDEARING GIRL

With you, live the best
To always love life.
Your body against my heart
Your belly to give life.

We will build love, every day.
We will build life with love.
I will offer you my doubts and certainties.

I love your silences and your voluble moments,
Tears of happiness; almost anything dresses you up!
My life, my twenty years... You were just a thought...
And I was waiting for you, my witch of happiness.

With a smile, you bewitch my ideas
And enchain my freedom at your feet.
I collect your moments of happiness
Slips me, every day, into your heart.

And you make your man, lying on the floor,
The happiest lover on earth.

AFTER LOVE....

On the beach, lying on her back, a white jersey smiles.
She is on vacation. She gets up. Bells ringing
Against her white skin. The white thong stuck between her globes
Scotch the Artist's gaze. More sand on the towels...

Next to her, a teenager shoots a young brunette
By the feet and throws her into the water. Out of game. On purpose.
The other blonde, apple green swimsuit on tanned skin,
Offers the sun her generous shapes. She smiles at the man.

He's somewhere else, under the coconut trees. He caresses the legs
of his gazelle.
Her smile intoxicated him. He would not have imagined such
happiness.
Introducing her, his friend had warned him: "-Above all, don't fall
in love! »

Two thousand kilometers. Droplets dripping on the skin.
Tattoos in the hollow of the lower back. Leaden sunshine.
Blonde with sunglasses is smoking a cigarette.

Green jersey, on his back, takes the pose of a Greek statue With
piercing, tattoos and cigarettes. . . Times have changed.
In his head, he goes from one to the other. They love him.
How fortunate! The Artist dreams to be loved by as many people as
possible.

Because he sees what others don't. Sensuality.
The soles of the feet masked in their sand gangue.
They're coming back from the water. He keeps drawing.
A perfect curve overflows the bikini. Here you go! A birth task...

Once again the vision of imaginary Africa.
Is she still thinking about him?
If only life were easier; one day she told him
That he was everything to her... that she loved him...

He believed her.
Under her feet, she cracked the vertebrae of his existence.

How can you feel so good...? And then nothing!

THE CAT WOMAN

Beautiful woman behind a cat mask,
With a mutinous smile, show off your bait.
You walk your nonchalant actress silhouette
Mix on your color palette, carefree.

Since the Cannes Film Festival, your noble Pygmalion
On the red carpet imposed you, with the energy of a lion,
You dance life, at every party,
Music and colored light spots.

Around you, admirers are legion,
Offer their love to you with ostentation.
How many would want to stick your hair in their mouths?
Lie your body under their chest, on their diaper?

And you, you sail, soul insensitive to their cries,
Hair in the wind, masked silhouette, kicked.
Have they forgotten that at night, all cats are grey?
Impossible, you continue on your way to infinity.

To your destiny as a muse, diva, égérie,
Inspirational inique of the author of this series.

THE MURDERER OF PASSING TIME

The Mediterranean Sea shines with its white sparks
On its three cold colors : turquoise, green and navy blue.
The sky is clear. Not any cloud. On the horizon slips a sailboat.

On the sand, everyone is settled. Very conventional installation.
Why am I the only one, lying on my stomach, face towards the sea?
The lack of money is killing me; I'm killing time with words...

All around me, the colored spots of the swimsuits,
Dark glasses on unknown faces. Thick thighs,
Droplets stuck on unnamed legs.

Everywhere, down to earth, face to face, the Artist dreams.
Ideas escape, he catches up with them with words and drawings.
He is obsessed with women; he would like to draw them all...

Smell of hot French fries and solar amber. It's two o'clock.
It's holidays. The water is too cold. He's alone.
Two or three windsurfing boards run in the distance.
The Artist dreams and happily thinks about the passing of time.

BEACH HOLIDAYS

First we are struck by the color of the water.
A light blue, between turquoise and emerald.
Then the rollings stones that twist your ankles,
Despite the flip-flops. Grey or sometimes beige pebbles
With white veins.

On the napkin rollers, multicolored splashes,
The traces of man who masks the traces of nature.
And then the worries begin; you have to make room.

Near this group of blondes with smooth, golden skin
Or these two brown caramel gals in panther swimwear.
A ponytail listens to Lenny Kravitz in her headset.

A silhouette in yellow pants makes her hair dance
And masks her eyes behind wide golden glasses.

Here, three insignificant boys wear orange T-shirts
Watched the airbag below the neck of a somewhat distant stretched
one.
Grandpa in a sailor's cap took his folding chair
And his wrinkled shepherdess twists her neck behind her tanned
look.

Smiles and enthusiastic attitudes for some
And the scowl of a pretentious bourgeois woman on a scratched sheet.
The hair is loose and the skirts are pleated.

Lacoste bags are placed between their grocery bags from Lidl or Ed;
It's just that we're on the broke beach. It's "deep France".
Momo offers pralines, Rachid drops a doughnut.
The spicy brunettes are harassed by watermelons,

Then cans and pareos, in shimmering colors, too bright.
They don't want the panther-like glitter flip flops.
Anyway, they didn't take much change,
Only their Motorola to pose under a refreshing umbrella.

A not wealthy young single man chose a book and his water bottle.
He pretends to focus on a sentence, for the eighth time
While green bikini put some oil on her pretty amber body.

In the distance, decorated parachutes take off from outboards
In front of the palaces and luxury hotels with renovated facades.
You can also hear the crash of jet skis and the bursts of laughter
From tanned young girls, in bikinis by designer's CD, YSL, D&G...

But a white barrier separates these two worlds on the beach of Nice.
Here, the only distraction is the haggling with Boubou.
A fifty years old director, chest pepper and especially salt,
Focuses on the SMS he prepares, his abdomen dilated,
While the coach lady rests, asleep on her stomach,
Collecting sunburns on her calves and on her back.

Around them, dialects mix, girls wearing too much make-up speak
loudly
Under the pretext of a tanned breast, they want to be noticed
While on the other beach, her silicone chest attracts her court, in
silence.

Bleached blonde dreams of a massage around her foot ring
Next to her, a detective novel: The murdered summer.
There comes a time when the bikinis are dry. The burning of sun
Can't even get the sleepy tourists to switch position of their body.

Comes the moment of dressing up; black and white bikini has
disappeared under jeans
And panther body tries to expose herself under a bath sheet
With the effigy of Lara Croft or Pamela Anderson.

Virile eyes are taped as soon as they can see
A fragment of white flesh, a breast, a foot under tanned leg.
Frail little girls take back their air mattresses; it's desolation.

Barely awaken, the only female teacher remains, proud to show off
A flaccid breast, a soft buttock with "Bon Chic Bon Genre" who just
finished his water bottle
But didn't learn anything from his chopped reading; he will read it
again tomorrow and the following days.

Grandpa gets his fingers stuck trying to fold up his chair.
Grandma puts on her glasses and finishes her bottle of "Antesite".
Rachid complains because he didn't sell all his doughnuts
And the scrunchy salesman plagues that it's not like it used to be.

Beach girls will shower, get ready, dress in black.
They will wear a chain at their ankle, a piercing at the navel.
There are still children running and screaming in the golden liquid,
Under the light and dark reflections of the last rays of light.
Soon they'll be back to school. So, until the end, they take advantage
Of beach' holidays.

BEACH LIFE

The sun ends its mad course towards the sea
It is still blinding the dark glasses before going to bed.
Beautiful beloved one sleeps on her towel with her beautiful black skin.
The bath sheet has golden suns with rhinestones and sequins./ glitter and glam.

Light blue swimsuit enhances chocolate and honey skin
Sleeping on Egyptian cotton, brown streaks fly away.
The boys of the sylph mummy in the orange bikini
Splashed fine gravel on a couple of elderly people.

Grandpa, bars afficionado, makes arm wrestling.
He's abusing the Métis child.
To make Grandma forget the sun's stings. Sexy green and yellow
flip-flops just passed twenty centimeters from my cheek
While tanned shorts play his bossa nova guitar.

Beautiful beaches have just woken up. It's a little cold.
I'm here. The goose bumps invade the top of her breasts.
By jerks and jerks, the poor sounds of the junk low-cost DJ insult your ears.
An evening will be improvised, in a brand-new place.

Asian black jersey deflates the light blue duck-headed buoy
While the red-haired yellow jersey finishes folding her boat
To the plastic windows. She cleans her little daughter's feet.

In the warm waters, two newly arrived antique ladies
Slide the flowers of the multicolored lycra from their jerseys
Menopausal combinations on the aspirin of their skins.

Foretelling the evening pizzas, a smell of charcoal burning Encourages
the stomachs. A kid calls his mother.
Reassuring mother comes to rescue the little girl. It smells like burnt.
They will love the cheese inflated on the puffed-up dough.

BEACH GIRLS

Beach girls have tanned bodies.
Under a blazing sun, they make you dream.
For a sarong, they know how to bargain.
Their bikini, you can admire it but not touch it...
Uninvited.

Beach girls. Beach girls.
They're beautiful like in the magazines.
That's because they read magazines,
Beach girls. Beach girls.

Beach girls often go in pairs.
Or as a group of warriors when they go hunting
The guys. They offer their backs and legs, too classy,
So that we can put some oil or milk. If they order.
And we go back by two, hand in hand....

Beach girls. Beach girls.
They're beautiful like in the magazines.
That's because they read magazines,
Beach girls. Beach girls.

Beach girls are setting up real ambushes
Speaking loudly about the clubs they're going to dance tonight.
They will shower, get ready, dress in black.
And when they dance, you only focus on them...
Beach girls are the most beautiful.

Beach girls. Beach girls.
They're beautiful like in the magazines.
That's because they read magazines,
Beach girls. Beach girls.

Next year, when you look for them, say "it's stupid",
Beach girls, beach girls, beach girls.
It is difficult to recognize them in their wiser outfits
They wear a chain around their necks, drag a stroller.

They look around them, with a little pinch in their heart
Their younger sisters, with a little mocking smile,
Who have just become the new girls of the beaches....

Beach girls. Beach girls.
They're beautiful like in the magazines.
That's because they read magazines,
Beach girls. Beach girls.

WAKE UP ON THE SAND

Under the cloudless azure dance the palm trees.
The wind draws volutes on beach towels
With flights of fine sand. He's hungry.

Lying on his stomach, his face sheltered behind his bag,
On his artist's notebook, he writes about his life.
He looks for inspiration in the bodies of stretched women.

The golden globes of a beloved blonde violate her privacy.
German or Polish, the young woman poses
A siren. A ring on each foot. She is not a fish.

The water is cold, blue and clear. She, in a lamé jersey,
Talk to a friend. He, in a dream, lies on top of her
And she laughs. However, it is elsewhere...

He only thinks of the other, at least two thousand kilometers away,
The ray of sunshine on her chocolate skin when she wakes up,
Her black skin, her coconut smell, the subtle taste
Of her lips....

Can you imagine a better breakfast?

A FEW WORDS
ON THE GO

Sweet as a wild almond, she wakes up,
Still all disheveled from sleep. Ten o'clock.
He calls her early. He is in St Tropez. She went out the day before,
To Paris. Every word is a sensual kiss.

She's been waiting for him. For months. He dreams of her.
She wants to take a shower, but don't want him to hang up.
They cling to a memory. No more than ten minutes,
In the subway corridors.
A few words; they loved each other too much.

In his nightly reveries, every night,
She tramples her absences, gags her silences.
He lies down in front of her; she takes a cigarette.
-"Tell me everything about your dreams!" she said. He obeys.

He imagines the traces left by the black skin
Staying too long on her back. He worships her.
She whips her mockery and the extra miles.
He's coming. He's coming.
She's ready. She's ready.
She's waiting for him.

Azed - St Tropez on 2007 August 26th

DUEL OF THE PRESENT TIMES

The mixed race with her amethyst eyes has a sad soul.
Behind her sunglasses, she rounds up her hunger for me
In the roundness of her smoking volutes.

A tall blonde girl makes her jewelry shine.
Her golden heart surrounded dances under her chain.
She's pretending to ignore me. But her heart is racing.
Only 22 years old. Almost as much separates us.
She already knows how to make the bracelets ring on her ankle.

The half-breed watches the scene in silence. Too discreet.
In her heart the music of the islands... "The guys' land". He's alone.
She would like him to ask her to dance. He doesn't know that.

He, silent, focused, searches his notebook.
Easy to make a film, golden skin against tanned skin....
She dances, but the music stops....The dream is broken.

Rose and golden gal makes the fine sand fly over her skin.
Her freshly manicured nails shine on contact with the water.
Disappointed, brunette with sunglasses leaves the game…
And definitively leaves his life.

I never saw her again.

TURN THE PLAGUE OF THE BEACH

It took a lot of thunderstorms
Before we can turn the page.
How many cries, how many tears
Before you lower your weapons.

The passing of time, enemy of humanity,
You often waste your time
And you swim, and I rage, and I wait for you,
Ruminant insanities in silence,

I wanted to be hot as a fire
Looking at your ass I'm freaking
With pleasure. You know how much I love it,
But you collect moments of hate.

I've earned them, these grains of sand.
And the sun. And the waves. Your screams,
You've made me sick and tired of it.
And, finally, you smile.

THE MAN WHO DIDN'T KNEW

He was tall. She was beautiful.
He was the one, she was the one
They had met in the corridors
Of the subway. He loved her black skin.

One day, between Rotunda and champagne,
They had found each other. From Aubagne
To Gemenos, they laughed all the time,
But he didn't dare to tell her....
I love you.

With her, he had found his happiness
But he couldn't reveal his heart.
She laughed, gained confidence, but saw nothing coming.
He was proud to belong to her.

The pictures of white teeth on the computer
Remind to the dead heart the traces of happiness
The man had not known....
Keep her close to his heart.

One evening, between Rotunda and Pastis,
She told him that it was all over.
They were swimming in memories, bitter,
Without picking up their own happiness on land.

The man didn't know, with a ring,
Tell her how much he loved her... no kidding!

CHECK MATE

You, my inspiring muse, do you know how much your absence
weighs on me?
Sumptuous beauty, ice-brown, sometimes angel, sometimes plague,
Do you know how empty are my days since you've been away from
me?

You took pleasure in wandering around the scene of your childhood.
I would have liked so much to have accompanied your discoveries,
Lush forests, canoes on wild rivers.

I had imagined so many landscapes with huge trees
The savannas traversed by wild animals, my wild
Life Partner, your inexhaustible palaver with slender gazelles
With velvety chocolate legs, as long as lianas.

No constraints for a while. No cell phone.
A healthy and natural life, far from night clubs and traffic jams.
This is *Too Much In Too Soon*, and money mourns poverty.
Purchases are followed by the frustrations of other improbable
purchases.

All alone, you left. I couldn't get over it!
Have a good trip to your roots. Here, my bottom has taken root
On the chair in front of the computer where I write dreams of
greatness,
The grim reality catches up with me. I'm not a slacker.

THE LOW-COST BEACH INTO THE CITY

The clear blue sky chases away a last cloud, as the horizon unfolds.
Children's cries are joyful. The splashes sing the song of life.
Business suits have given way to multicolored spots.
Wet swimsuits let sparkle the colors of life.

Children are beyond themselves. A bucket draws a circle of droplets
And the tanned chicks pretend to run. The geysers are dancing,
Fugitive white spots slamming on translucent waters.
Behind the buoys, still sails. Not a bit of wind.

A teenager buried his brother. The brown head protrudes from the
sand, Laughing. Parents are asleep, thinking about naughty naps.
The towels are too small or too exuberant.

Women show the amber color of their skin,
The curved shape of their nail polish. The small breasts
Side by side with the too opulent and firm, from the surgeons' works.

Some of them are eye-catching: one is pregnant, the other is veiled.
All around, it's the ballet of framed tanned skins
Colors, always identical and always new,
Swimsuits. A pleasure for the eyes!

Languages are unknown; the range is multi-ethnic.
Men are even paler as they have responsibilities
Men are even more tanned they have money.

They hide their bellies under glasses and a box cap,
But their ugly old-fashioned jersey speaks for them.
Young women are beautiful. The others don't look good.
Is there any age that makes you lose all traces of femininity?

Lover couples frolic in new and trendy swimsuits.
He's lying on his back. She comes to kiss her property.
Women wear dark glasses with letters on the side.
Men make sand castles, dreaming of real estate projects.

All around, the city breathes the incoherence of a shoddy architecture.
No harmony in the buildings stacked around fitted hangars.
Among this hubbub of screams and concrete hodgepodge, four letters
On a yellow background surrounded by blue: Lidl. The rallying cry
of a broke youth.

Because the city is poorer than its suburbs, created by fishermen,
Inhabited by the unemployed and assisted, looking for new subsidies.
Without any shame, an adult displays his intimate lingerie, underwear
from the supermarket,
And children are running around with their naked butts. An
economy for Mama.

The Beach is next to the Breeze. The Stopover is next to the inevitable
Blue Lagoon.
On the beach, there is always a black guy with glasses, earring and
shaved head
Above his black jersey, a multitude of abdominal muscles.
Well, I didn't even know we had a muscle there!

And further on, the incredible platinum blonde in a leopard bikini.
She draws attention to her stone-washed denim shorts.
No doubt that she is Miss Beach-nightclub. There is always one.
The one that all women hate and men bless.

When their risk-taking is unlucky at *pétanque*,
They find themselves thirteen to zero, lowered eyes under the quolibets,
And hope, in secret, that the platinum blonde is named Fanny.
But Fanny is brunette and has a hairy butt. They close their eyes.

They will return home in the evening with many memories of their holidays.
The good value for money. It didn't cost them a penny.
The children are already in bed. Housewives started their washing machine
At a reduced rate. They close their eyes and try to remember...

A TASTE OF ETERNITY

Carnivorous flower, against my body.
Between your smooth thighs, I bite.
Your apricot calls my hopes high
And destroyed the horrors of despair,
Every night.

Angel with generous shapes,
Smile of a sulfurous tigress,
Your wings stretched towards the future
We will drive in excess.
As we go along.

Will you be the first black dove
With a diamond sparkle smile?
Thin silhouette with a bomb body,
You enchant your lover's dreams.
Just like before.

I'll always have your bare feet against my skin,
An old hell to warm up, an oripeau.
The heat will burn your nights on your diaper,
And the sweat will stick your hair in my mouth.
Before the shower.

NEVER MIND

What are the beautiful hands of a watch for?
If every second I think about you?
The nights are so long. I'm afraid of the dark, on the right,
Since you've been so far away, so far away from me.

I dial your "zero six" on my iPhone
But I always hang up before you pick up.
So far away, so alone, makes me phone.
I'd like to put you on the spit.

I'm not telling you, darling,
How much my boredom is bleeding! I miss you.
It's up to the man to call his sweetheart!
Out of my sight, you forget me, you acrobat.

I dial your "zero six" on my iPhone
But I always hang up before you pick up.
So far away, so alone, makes me phone.
I'd like to put you on the spit.

With you, I wanted to be smart,
Make you languish, fish by line....
Time has interfered, my love.
Always there for you, I'll wait for you to come back.

I dial your "zero six" on my iPhone
But I always hang up before you pick up.
So far away, so alone, makes me phone.
I'd like to put you on the spit.

DRUNK WITH YOUR TROUBLES

I walk alone, thoughtful, along the harbor
My sister is waiting for me in a coffee shop in St Tropez.
A man accosted me, so handsome, so strong.
But I don't know him. Quick, a coffee! What a nerve!

She asks me why I still love you.
I got you under my skin, in my soul, in my body.
Music, champagne and high heels, at midnight,
You know, honey, I'm a night bird.

I read your words, sitting on the edge of the platform.
Your book tells me your troubles. Respect me.
And if I want to, soon I'll be yours
For a convoluted love game.

Only music helps me to survive
When memories about you make me drunk.
Music, champagne and high heels, at midnight,
You know, honey, I'm a girl from the night.

She asks me why I still love you.
I got you under my skin, in my soul, in my body.
Music, champagne and high heels, at midnight,
You know, honey, I'm a night bird.

LIKE A TASTE OF COMING BACK

I never thought I'd hurt you,
I didn't want to bring you any pain.
When I made fun of your curves.
You know that at home, all you are is what I love.

I just wanted to get you into my car.
Living at 200 miles an hour, escaping an empty existence.
I wanted to slip every inch of my love into you
Deep down in your life, without any detour.

Today, if you came back, I would catch you
Against the walls of bitterness and regret
With passion, savagely, I will lie you down
On the tables of life, by force and on your own free will.

Love is an idiotic symphony without law or example.
I want to engrave you in my life and embed myself into your life.
You will be my gemstone and I will be the music that springs forth
When you open the case. Our love will be an example.

Today, if you came back, I would catch you
Against the walls of bitterness and regret
With passion, savagely, I will lie you down
On the tables of life, by force and on your own free will.

THE SUNNY EYES

The angel with the sunny eyes tells me that she loves me.
I've been waiting for her for so long, I didn't see it coming.
Love always comes when you don't expect it
And sends you on a cloud; it's your future.

The archangel with wheat hair plays with colors.
She likes to change, to transform herself to better surprise.
Brown or red hair lady, her eyes are glowing
When my hands run on guitars to spread it out.

The angel with lips of love can sing with a wonderful voice
And dancing, better than an MTV princess. That's her.
She knows how to do everything better than others; she is happy.
She is so beautiful that I can only see her.

Yet, the angel with the sunny eyes, I will never tell her That I love her.
Love is too fragile. It's a ritornello.
Years of love and, for one word too many, risk losing it forever.
It's better this way! The angel with the sunny eyes is the most beautiful.

IT'S NOT FOR YOU

They were beautiful and appetizing,
The three of them, lying on the fine sand.
The drops were dripping on their buttocks and breasts
And they turned around, constantly, languishing.

There were three of them, young and beautiful to munch.
Talking nonsense, giggling, squirming
And the more I looked at them, the more I fell for them.
We should have made a choice; no choice is more tempting!

Come back to Earth, these girls are not for you.
Come down to Earth; you can't pick up all three.

When the sand would stick to their thighs
And that their beautiful breasts looked like ripe fruit
Gorged with sunshine, they stood up, leaned against a wall
Then they went to the sea, all eyes taped to their thighs.

The sirens of everyday life have beautiful tanned legs
And sunglasses imitating Cartier. One balloon is enough
To highlight their chest, buttocks and tanned back.
Their thongs are as many splashes of color. And worse!

Come back to Earth, these girls are not for you.
Come down to Earth; you can't pick up all three.

When they got back on their bath towels,
Dripping droplets on the caramel of their skin,
Covered in white sand on their feet and hands,
They looked like Greek statues, all made of marble and skin.

A boy came up to me with goggles on his nose.
He offered to get to know them and sat down
Next to them. He was staring at them like a lost man.
They laughed in his face,
Mocked each other nicely. He got up and left, stale.
So, I told him:

Come back to Earth, these girls are not for you.
Come down to Earth; you can't pick up all three.

FOR THOSE WHO KNOW HOW TO WAIT

How many nights spent scratching paper until late,
Waiting for you, imagining you, my velvet goddess. Thoughts for you.
How many words written or whispered on guitar strings
Which will never be the love song I dream of for you.

You like to dance, have fun with boys your own age
As I used to like to do, too, when I dreamed of being good.
You know, love always comes for those who wait.
These words resonate in my head; I will learn them.

Too often love has come knocking on my door
For a night or two, hot and wild, against a wall, against a door.
Today, for you, I venture into all the rifts
Of your love and your body. Without limit, I fight a battle.

You know, love always comes for those who wait.
These words resonate in my head; I will learn them.

I have known loves so distant, so distant, so long ago
Without ever looking back on my past. I don't have any more time.
From now, it's you I want, to curl up and love you
For it is you I want to look at; it is you I want to keep.

You know, love always comes for those who wait.
These words resonate in my head; I will learn them.

COME

Come and join me soon
In my lonely sleep.

I feel, in me, dawning
This desire so deep
Which explodes when your body explodes
Lies down next to me....

Come quickly,

Come and join me soon
In my interplanetary awakening
Where I feel in you
To fear this pleasure so fertile
That explodes inside me

When your lonely body joins me
In my sleep,
It's extraordinary.

A woman who falls asleep and awaits you.

COME QUICKLY

Come quickly
To join me
In my sleep
Lonely.

Come quickly
lengthen your body
that awakens in me,
the deepest desire,

the one who starts from the toes
and reaches the root
of my body.

I love you.

A woman who likes to lie down.

THIS NEED TO WRITE...

I snapped at the sight of your pad of paper.
Laying nonchalantly on the table.
He was screaming for me to come closer to him,
With my lipstick or a big red marker
To write your first name in letters of fire
Alain immediately followed by your Isabelle.

Then I would have surrounded them with a red circle,
With this very special shape, curved upwards,
And stretching down to the point. To make it beat harder.

But I resisted the temptation of happiness immediately satisfied
To keep only the pleasure and an even more intense desire
Caused by these voluntary prohibitions not yet accomplished.

AZ I love U. Isa.

A woman who draws with her lipstick.

FRESH LOVE

Warmth of your face,
Face turned towards me

And I'm waiting for you, tense,
In the felted softness
From your apartment.

Join me, join me quickly,
Come quickly into my arms,
So that, they can finally draw from your soul,
All the joys you give me....

For four days now.

A woman in love who languishes.

TWO WEEKS ALREADY

From the height of your sleep, I dominate your body.
You dream, sleepy, curled up on your side.
Are you drunk with fatigue, happiness or love?
Unless you're drunk on me, that's all!

This afternoon, I've known you for two weeks.
Will you be here in fifteen years? Will we live another day?
Would I still be, right here, looking at your black hair,
To breathe in your smell, to listen to the murmur of your voice
Who shares your dreams with mine.

I would so much like to share your fantasies, live your secrets.
Your heart against my body, you're there, lying,
On the side of our bed of love.
Today, love rhymes with humor.

I'll be alone tonight with my bottle of champagne
And my cigarette. So alone without your voice!
I think I'll give my life to live again this moment
There, near you, dreaming very strongly of you,
To dream, quite simply I love you.

TO FEED OUR LOVE

My darling Alain,

If you had been with me, I could have easily fasted,
I think so, because love is the food you never get enough of.
It could not have been so. Never mind that!
Can you forgive me?

I missed you, and your presence
I thought it was essential to this void of absence.

I love you so much. I believe in your tenderness and love.
Share my existence with you, live together,
To respect and love us,
That's what I wish the world most now.

My body is in a state of wakefulness, without you.
All you need now is your desire to wake up, suddenly,
The demons of desire burning in me.

Come quickly...

A woman who is very hungry for you, dear love.

TO THE MAN WHO SLEEPS BESIDES ME

I love you with all my heart, with all my soul
Even if my behavior this weekend was very unpleasant.

I'm tired, irritated, but despite my distance,
I'm only thinking of taking holidays with you.

Yesterday, I watched you sleep, so peaceful,
You looked like a pure and sensitive child.
I was so eager to keep this little minute,
So that it will last forever. But hush!

Excuse me, forgive me for these mood swings.
Which, despite everything, are only a proof of love.
You are, more and more, the man I love so much
At this minute and for thousands more, again.

A wounded woman who heals herself with love.

SMALL GOLDEN RAT

My little golden rat,

The days go by and I love you even more.
There's not a morning I don't wake up happy
To be by your side and push you around to watch
Your little disheveled head, all full of sleep.

There is not a minute in the day without me having
The desire to hold you very tightly to soak up your scent,
Taste the warmth of your being.

You come back later, and I like to open the door for you.
I like that minute when you look at me.
And you're taking me hard against you.

I look forward to the door closing on the outside
So that we can start our one-on-one love life
Which extends late into the night.

I love you.

A woman who likes doors if her man is behind.

VENICE, ONE DAY

I wake up, all dishevelled,
Eyes still swollen
By the lack of your sleep.

I'm thinking of you,
As loud as the day
Where we loved each other for the first time.

I can't wait to go to Venice together/with you.
We'll leave our worries behind
At the gateway to the city

And then we can finally say to each other:
Let the party begin!

We will mention Baudelaire,
Think of loving at leisure, loving to die
To the country that looks like you....

See you tonight, to see a new day
Getting up with you.

A woman who dreams of romantic journeys.

SUN AND SPARKS

The man I love is a sensitive and kind being,
Hardened in this very special alloy,
He is both man and child, emperor and Peter Pan
Laughing, crying, never the same and yet...
From time to time so annoying.

The dawn rises on his life and yet,
Sometimes it's like he finished it.
Approaching his thirties, he sees that it is high time To affirm his existence and to be independent.

The man by my side was born to shine, And he will, certainly.
If he considers that after dawn,
The sun will shine until the dawn of time. I love you.
A woman with eyes full of sparks.

SECRET MURMUR

It was some time ago, but it was also yesterday.
It was grey around me and suddenly a light.

Your face approached mine.
I squeezed my hands very tightly
And I said a prayer, a little nothing.

Today, my body is in turmoil,
A part of your body is inside me.

I live your presence, feel your caresses,
Love your beloved body, lying on my butt.

This prayer to the beloved man,
I whisper it, silently, at night, at your bedtime.
I bless your body and your heart when they open to me
And I dive into it with pride.

Anything can happen, now nothing matters anymore.
Five months have already passed
But it was only yesterday when the man approached
And kissed me that my life changed.

THE CRACK IN THE AZURE

It's suddenly the crack.
The Earth opens its inside and sucks me down to the bottom.
The thunder dances in my voice.
The tearing rain is rolling down my cheeks,
Crystal beads in front of which you remain helpless.

It is all the anguish that is breaking out,
Like the hurricane destroying everything in its path,
And leaving me alone in front of a grey wall
With no windows to give me any hope.

These are the hours of suffering of the past
Coming back at a gallop, fears and tears,
All these questions about my present life
In which I invest my last efforts.

Blessed hours when you come home and hug me,
Cursed lonely hours with memories gnawing at me.
Tender hours or count only your face, your look and your voice.
Delightful hours when I enjoy you from head to toe.

You for whom the days would be nights, if you were not at my side.
Alain, you live in my heart.
For one day to be one with you, always you.
Always you making me lose my mind,
It's you, it's me and that's life.

Take my heart, possess my body,
Set your doubts and hopes in my existence.
Alain, at my side, you turn into a stone arch
So the cracks in my life may span and fade

In the landscape, you are rebuilding, stone by stone.

Alain who is strong, who sometimes cries and whom I love
Because it is the sun that could have burst the grey wall
Which had always surrounded my existence.

I love you.

A woman looking through the wall.

PRAYER TO
THE MAN I LOVE

I am a barren land or nothing, not even the craziest love,
Cannot make the slightest little being germinate in my body so
bruised.
I'm a sterile spirit who desperately needs his fertilizer
To make the most beautiful ideas mature, the most fluid writing.

Love me, love me very much to overcome this nothingness.
Fertilize my mind to give birth to a new life.
Caress my body like you never dared before,
Whisper to me "I love you"
To transcend my pleasure to exist.

I want to be two and inhabit your body,
I want through my eyes so clear,
You could see the reflection of the man I love,
The one I believe in and admire.

My respect for his personality is only matched by his dreams
And his moments of intense love and his wildest desires.
My passion for his body reaches inaccessible heights
When he enjoys/comes through all the pores of his skin....
And shouts his pleasure in/to the face of the world.

We play together for true love, for the purest and strongest,
To the one who makes us leave all the taboos in the cloakroom.
Love, creator of dreams that can finally be realized, inspiring love.
Our creativity will be born from the balance and respect of our bodies.
I pray that the man who loves me will ejaculate his strength to create,
May he finally fertilize my hope, one day, building a cathedral.

LIVE!

Have mercy on the living, shouts my soul to me
But I live with my dead, very much mine.
The only things that no one can take from me
Since they are nothing but a few traces in the memories.

It dulls my appetite for life, this latent death,
 It numbs my limbs with thousands of ants
Until I impregnated its repulsive coldness into my heart.

This morbid fascination makes my little icy body shudder with horror,
Frozen by fear and lucidity, certainty without hope
That she'll finally get me at the turn, the black hooded bitch.

But I will resist this panic fear all my life.
Take the straight line and keep an eye on it,
This may be my lifeline. To live!

I HURT YOU

Why do I always have to wait for these painful moments ?
The little sting there, just on the most sensitive point of my being,
To extract all those things, I'd like to tell you
But that I will hide again and again...

That part of mystery that is part of my image,
Maybe the one you love, I don't know...

I feel bad for you and I enjoy it every time I meet you,
Stealthy happiness but so intense,

I'm hurting you and I'm dying to tell you
I have trouble conjugating the verb come together.

A possessive woman who no longer wants to suffer.

THANK YOU FOR EVERYTHING

Unconsidered thanks to the man
Who picked me up from the hospital,
Phoned to check in with me,
He came home quickly to help me
Shopping, preparing dinner
And specially to share it with me.

Unconsidered thanks to the beloved man
For sharing with the woman
That you claim to love These sweet moments.

Unconsidered thanks to the absent man
Not to wake up at all
When you get back.

Above all, thanks for not hearing
Your apologies!

A woman who, stupidly, is waiting for you.

I THINK AND
YOU ACT

It hurts so much today....
I think of you and tears run down.
I feel empty, depressed, useless.
What would I do if I didn't have you and my mother to help me?

The money I spent was not for me
And it wasn't a sudden impulse, a wind of madness
For something futile and fleeting
But simply to be able to live decently
And have a minimum of comfort and luxury.

Also, when I see the future,
I wonder what more I'm going to do,
Restrict to what?
I wanted you to be happy, not want for anything,
And that's where it got me... got us.

Fortunately, love cannot be bought
Because we'd be out of business 24 hours a day.
Love is free, it comes from the heart
And it's good to have you with me, close to me.

Alain, when we live in luxury and comfort,
You'll still be there to enjoy it first.
I promise you, it will be soon.

I love you as much as ever. I miss you already.
I can't wait tonight to hold you tight against me.

A woman in tears who repented.

I'M FREAKING OUT, IT'S THE FLOP

I am the black knight,
With a pure heart but a black soul.
For six centuries, every night,
I'm hanging around, having lost all hope.

I'm looking for the green diamond of your life
Who alone can save me from hell. You're laughing.
One day, in your femininity, you appeared
And in front of you, I found myself naked.

Love can break everything,
I asked for it.
It doesn't matter if I go to hell,
Without you, I have nothing else to do.

I'm your one-night stand,
Knight in black leather armor.
Without you, I hang out from bar to bar.
But it may be not too late.

I'm working on an electric pinball machine.
To the sound of an electronic blues.
I mean, like a green diamond, you reappeared
And forever, the dark thoughts have disappeared.

Love can break everything,
I found you so I wouldn't leave you again.
It doesn't matter if you drag me to hell,
Without you, I wouldn't have anything else to do.

WARNING!

My beloved Alain,

Yes, I'm taking my favorite pen to write you a note.
I don't apologize for these mood swings.
Which are a normal reaction to an abnormal situation.

I don't want our lives to become a meeting place,
That our house looks like a pass hotel
Where you can guess and love each other from 10 to 11 or 5 to 7.

I can't stand not having a weekend, parties,
To see and talk to you, basically, 4 to 5 hours a week.
I say, "Enough!" because I don't want to continue like this anymore.

The days go by and I love you even more.
There's not a morning I don't wake up happy
To be by your side and push you around to watch
Your little dishevelled head, all full of sleep.

There is not a minute in the day without me having
The desire to hold you very tightly to soak up your scent,
Taste the warmth of your being.

You come back later, and I like to open the door for you. I like that
minute you look at me.
And you're taking me hard against you.

I look forward to the door closing on the outside
For that we can start our one-on-one love life
Which extends late into the night.
I love you.
A woman who likes doors if her man is behind.

DIVORCE IN 16/9

For life, for better and for laughter!
We say yes to life, no to death!
Yes to envy, no to effort!

We wait longer when we marry young.
Women, they piss us off with their young years,
Their best years, you name it; we don't have a dime
And we end up at midnight at Mc Do in a tuxedo and an evening
dress.

To the one who shares my life, who wants to take all my nights,
I impose to share my boredom, the desires of a better world,
Desires without wishes, wishes without desire.

Romantic dinners with mini candles from Prisunic
It's about telling our troubles, our worries, our torments,
The horrors of a professional world where men have a title
And women a first name. Well done, feminists world!

Compliments declaimed in the flickering glow of the flame
Are as many pious images of immature dreams seen on TV:
A good job, a car, a nice house with a swimming pool
And especially a mega bank account. It's called happiness,
While it would only take an even bigger mega bank account.

And when we accomplished this difficult mission,
We learn the news in a 16:9 telegram:
I don't love you anymore, my love.

It's just a matter of age,
A question of love in the face of time passing.
Goodbye! Get in touch with my lawyer!

AN EXCLUSIVE LOVE

Honey, you tell me, you want a love merger.
Emotions in silence, feelings without effusion.
A prince charming in a white suit
Without his possessive mother and bloody brothers.

No Saturday night singing friends either
Unable to release the chosen one before dark night.

You want a unique, magical and great lordly love
Days and nights singing to you: "My heart..."
Restaurants, opera, St Tropez, Cavalaire,
Without any mention of his work or any banking ban.

You want to be his only princess
And that he spends hours talking about the color of your eyes.

Love is your religion, baby, virtue is your obsession.
What does modesty mean to a Pygmalion photographer
Used to reading the soul in the texture of the skin of the pretty
Young girls and women to make them even more beautiful.

You would like a serene world and a quiet life
When your warrior goes off to fight battles
Armed with his mobile phone and his bill collector.

You see, baby, the fairy tales' world has changed a lot.
Today what would be worth the feelings of being an eagle
In the henhouse of a life too narrow.

You want to be his only princess
And that he spends hours talking about the color of your eyes.
My sweetest, you are my only princess
And I'll spend my whole life studying your eyes.

LITTLE URBAN ROCK POEMS

ANTI-PICK-UP LINE

Young man looking for a young girl
Cheerful, friendly, positive, in love...

You, the girl I don't know anything.
And who reads these few words,
You who recognize yourself and seek
The one who already loves you, without knowing you,
Without even meeting you,

Know that if you read this word
That's because I chose you.
It is up to you to accept or refuse.

If you refuse, too bad for me, I won't insist;
I'll knock on another door.

But if you accept, come to me,
And give me your hand.
It's time to break the ice.

Let's go together to the other side of the mirror.

TO AN EGOMANIAC LADY

Do you know, in two thousand years,
When we will be no more than dust,
The world will continue to spin
And the sun to shine.

When the memories are gone
And that our names, forever forgotten,
Will decompose on rotten stone
From our deep tombs

We will be nothing more
When our bodies cease to exist.
Unless our angry souls
Do not float in purple spaces.

So, Baby, come drown yourself
In the icy ocean of my dreams
Including the thick and crystalline darkness
Free souls from their golden prison/jailhouse.

OPEN YOUR EYES
AND KISS ME

One day, in less than a century,
Your skinned corpse, covered in rot,
By your big blind eyes will be gnawed away by
The abundant vermin of necrophageous larvae.

Your eyes will burst under the repeated blows
That you will be subjected to sticky mandibles.
Earthworms and rats, covered with rubbish
Will tear your body apart, deformed by time.

On your virgin remains, once so pretty,
Will crawl on your flesh, swarms of vermin
That will cover you with poisonous kisses
And suck on your body, your vagina and your breast.

Under the muddy gangue and rotten boards
Those scumbags will drool over your bloodless corpse.
Because you'll only be a putrid carrion,
A mass of chairs with scattered bones.

When the disgusting dirt has punctured your stomach
Armies of spiders will nest in your bosom
And hordes of black excrementing cockroaches
Will penetrate your lips that once kissed.

Imagine the past, remember the future.

INSPIRATION?

What is this mysterious shadow
Breathing stories into me
And writing my poems?

This hand that takes mine
Fills my head with tales and news
And makes me tell them.

What is this fabulous being
Who dictates these words to me.

During the sweat oozes
Of my raped brain
And seems to be swirling
In incomprehensible delusions.

It's in my mind.
To his hand, my hand obeys;
She scratches the paper
Where the other one tells him to.

In these moments when I am no longer myself
Or I'm someone else,
Fear is tightening my throat,

The fear of one day seeing
This shadow disappear
And to be alone.
All alone, in front of the blank sheet of paper.

NICE TO MEET YOU

People call me by my parents' names,
Yet, if they knew...

I am the son of the Earth,
But Satan is my father.
I am the son of the Earth,
And the devil is my father.

I was born of Satan's love
And of some bewitching witch
Out of the depths of hell.

I defy time and money.
My only love is blood.
My name is Lucifer,
Master of the universe.

Sulfurous fumes from my hellish kingdom,
I came out of my mothers' womb, all hairy.
And with my velvet teeth I stroked them.

Of course, I killed, stole money,
Sucked blood, raped children
But I'm not guilty.

One evening, to repent the dead,
Pederast Oedipal, I kissed my father
With both my hands... stuck around his neck.

ALBATROSS, DAWN ACROSS

I would like to be an angel
To raise me from the mire
Who swallows up men
Who named it the world.

I would like to be a demon,
Gnawing at the entrails
Of an old man, so good
To prove to him that he is dead
The Watchmaker, who created
Time Space, man and life.

I want to escape this prison
Corrupted by men,
To find myself elsewhere
In a better world.

I want to fly, to kill the atmosphere,
Beyond the limits of the Earth.
I want to glide over the seas,
Feeling detached from my irons,
To penetrate the deep heavens
To finally surpass the horizon.

Like a bird covered with feathers,
Color of wisps,
Night and Day, around the Moon
And from elsewhere I would travel.

I would stay that way, for an eternity,
Lying in the sky, my white wings spread out
All my life, and well after my death;
But what would be the time that will no longer exist?

Today is a day that tomorrow will be dead.

LOVE IN A TRAIN

Saw her by chance in a train,
On a beach or in the street
Just long enough for us to regret
To see you leave.

With a hint of bitterness,
At the corner of the lips,
She makes you smile, gets up and still leaves.

You play with people's minds
And disappear, without a goodbye.

Let the door open and free you!
I was trying to hum
To pass the time.
But nothing was there; it was cold inside me.

Was it the hope of finding an uncertain love again?

Or just a pretext
To see you again, to talk to you
Trying to win you back, to enchant you.
Tearing up your cocoon
To make you even more beautiful.
Tearing your everyday face off
To find your soul inside.

LOVE IN ARMOR

I refuse to expose my heart
And I lock it in a shell
Thick, with spikes.

And when, in my arms,
I'm holding the girl I love,
It hurts me to think of making her suffer....

But I keep squeezing gently,
Let her breast rub against my thorns.

Until her own heart is bare
To find out if I can reveal mine to her.

HEY YOU, ZOMBIE !

Imagine, on a full moon night,
Crossing the alleys, framed with cypress trees,
Dark alleys of a sleeping cemetery!

It's past midnight and you're moving forward,
Spying on the slightest crunch on the slabs,
The furtive sound of your footsteps, along the headstones.

Suddenly a heartbreaking call comes out of a grave
And you hear your own name.
Imagine the anguish that suddenly embraces you.

Maybe this is a living dead man.
Buried alive, or some spirit of your parents?

Deaf to the fear that assails you,
You pick up the shovel that was lying around
And you dig, lifting the catafalque
Where the unfortunate shipwrecked man rests.

The shovel finally meets the worm-eaten coffin.
You destroy the rotten wooden lid
And before your eyes, a perfectly preserved corpse,
Lies, silent, a white worm moving on his belly.

You don't know him, but you help him.
With a branch, you remove this annelid
And the corpse decomposes into a fine dust
Full of filthy insects, rotten vermin...

You back away from the shock.
You look at his livid face

Staring at you with his big, blind eyes.
Because the half-buried carrion... is you.

You turn your eyes and fall into the vault
On this repulsive mass.
And you will die!

In the morning, everything is quiet in the cemetery.
But in a vault, a zombie like you
Waiting for his next victim...

TO ZERO !

Dreams broken like a big mirror that breaks
And terminates me with a terrible stabbing.

Love is not what it used to be.

A girl in my dreams,
Another one I remember,
And so many more to conquer.

THIEF

Female soul thief, you suck my brain
And break my heart. It's not nice!

You bewitched me to tie me up better,
And words and your fingernails tear me apart.

You hold my heart in your hands;
One word, and my future ends tomorrow.

My pretentious dreams, break them!
Don't let me destroy myself!

MY ANGEL, MY LOVE

Tell me! Are you that angel I saw before
Escaped from a world that disappeared too quickly?

Aren't you an aristocratic princess
Lost far away from the very old Hyperborée

With your pretty face with fair skin
With cheeks colored by a shy prude?

Wasn't it you I met once,
Slaying my sword against the traitors to your crown
To cover yourself with jewelry and finely carved gold?

I wish I could have been your page and your knight
In a heroic era in ancient times.
But today you're a young girl
Simple and soft, with a bewitching look.

Today you are a girl, I kiss you, you swoon.
Maybe you really are an angel
And if my lips ever finally touch yours
I can brave the wrath of all the gods.

Ishtar, herself, will no longer be able to break us apart
In this wonderful world, a paradise of love and beauty,
In this world of harmony and love
That we dreamed: The world of lovers.

BARBARIAN LOVE

Tell me about it! Are you an angel
Escaped from some missing world?

Aren't you that aristocratic princess
From the very old Hyperborea

With your thin, pale face
What does a chaste shyness color?

Wasn't it you I met once,
In those distant times and for whom
I fought, with a sword in each hand,
The enemies of your crown?

How many traitors, merchants and thieves
Did I kill to cover you in your sleep,
Finely carved gold and vermilion jewelry?

Haven't you forgotten these immemorial times?
Do you remember when you were queen.
And that I was your page?

For and by your eyes, I was even a dragon,
Watching over your diamonds, your countless wonders.

Today, the crowns have fallen.
You're a fashionable girl, beautiful and sweet
An almost woman of the timeless years
Whose bewitching eyes know how to keep me chained.

UTOPIA

AZed woke up one morning, With so much to say
That he had nothing more to say.

Sometimes, often words are not enough.
Thinking comes up against the wall of communication.
We realize that we can't change the world.

Wars will always exist,
Even with ten thousand anti-military films.
Think that God created man in his own image, as people said.

The man in his chair claims to be civilized
But shall we touch his little privileges
And he is again barbarian, ready to kill for pleasure....
What pleasure?

Politicians will continue their fine promises
To satisfy their only thirst for power and money/dough,
But the scandals will always be hushed up.

The people will continue to criticize them
And to vote for them in order to better criticize them.
It's so difficult to be the actor of your own life!

There will always be rich and poor,
Injustice, iron pots against soil/land pots,
And this feeling of unsatisfied revenge.

Hungry people will end up in the shade of jail for petty thieves,
An apple or a piece of bread when the untouchables
Will benefit from huge schemes, but committed in white collar.

There will always be pain and drama,
Suffering, betrayals and tears,
Because deep down, man is not so good.

Children will continue to starve,
And murderers of children will still get away with it
To continue unspeakable traffic....

You can't spend your life rebelling!
You might as well live your life and try to help as much as you can
Because deep down, the only inevitable outcome awaits us.

BLACK ANGEL,
WHITE ANGEL

Looking at some pictures, still wet with novelty,
My ears full of music that doesn't exist,
I discovered two delicate angels with blossoming shapes,
Stolen images of a film that would never exist.

My brain buried under the memories caresses the kisses.
Hiding their eyes under the mask of their thoughts,
Puppets made of women are discovered
Through a two-way mirror. Without glass, either. They laugh.

Paper memories, illusions of love and dreams,
I mentioned the images of a dreamy afternoon
And fantasies, fake loves, with the evanescent
Egyptian princess dressed as a smiling fairy.

Like a Pygmalion, in love with my models,
I turned them into glossy fantasies.
Illusions of love and dream, eyes surrounded by black circles,
They become the reality that makes us forget the other true reality.

Icarus fell from the bed into the arms of the black angel,
Samothrace without face, arms, wings, but beautiful,
She plays in the sheets the erotic games of the white angel.
Then she trades tiaras and necklaces for her daydreams.

While looking at some pictures, I discovered
That Christ was a young girl of the 21st century,
Who hid her eyes full of tears
Behind fake star's dark glasses, at night.

ROCK STAR FOREVER

When I'll be a Rock Star, I'll be a guitarist
With dark glasses and also a pianist.
I'll have makeup and androgynous masks
I will be the singer of the year. Every year.

When I'll be Rock Star, I'll have two entities:
One for my private life that you won't know about,
The other one on stage, dressed, wearing a black hat,
I'll play the killer behind my dark glasses.

When I'll be a Rock Star, I'll be eccentric
Often dressed in green, yellow and silver,
I'll put on my makeup for the purple scene
And I'll wear dresses, scarves, tunics.

When I'll be a Rock Star, I'll be loved
And I'll be able to choose from the crowd my new fiancées/girlfriends.
I'll make the music they inspired me
And, one by one, with must-have hits, I will launch them.

When I'll be Rock Star, I'll be the leader
Of the group of young girls who'll accompany me.
They will be as wonderful on stage as they are in bed
And, two by two, without jealousy, they will love me.

When I'll be Rock Star, I'll be decadent.
I'll play the androgynous, obsessed thugs.
Sitting for hours, I'll admire
My new make-up in the mirrors of my dressing room.

When I'll be Rock Star, I'll play aggressive electro rock.
My music will be symphonic and light.
My stage games will make my reputation
And, on a regular basis, I will change my brand image.

When I'll be a Rock Star, I'll bring music to life
From the 70s to 2050, it will be an exceptional love.
I'll be a genius, an artist, a rock poet.
The whole world will have its greatest Rock Star.

And you will like it and adore it.

KNIGHT OF THE NIGHT

AZed, the knight of the night,
Come in the evening, late, share my life
Unless he prefers
To blend into my night.

I can hear his footsteps resounding,
From the depths of my body,
His key opens the lock of my sensuality,
His voice makes my sexuality explode.

I want to have the hold of his senses,
Departmentalize his pleasure, violate his fantasies,
Trampling on his orgasms, swallowing his masculinity,
Exterminate his pain
To transform him gently.

I will spit my pleasure in his face.
He will join me and, when he falls back,
Exhausted with fatigue, I'll push him,
With my agile feet,

To the other side of the night,
The one of whispering and screaming
That are lived and not told.

A woman who dreams of chivalrous feelings.

UNCERTAIN FUTURE

I don't want to get old; I'm too scared.
And the future is uncertain.

I would so much like to kiss her with both my hands.
She has such clear, perverse eyes.

I feel like I'm going to crack to the bone.
The screams are so beautiful from the outside,
But rebelling is so vulgar!

The handcuffs of education remain welded
On my wrists... And I stay silent.

THE FINAL EXPLOSION

In the chaos following the final explosion
Time continues to finish his work.
Deaf to calls from the weaker sex.

The futuristic angel leaves the world to meditate.
He knows his place is elsewhere.

Anyway, Adam will wake up Eve.
Despite the cries of the last dying god.

Life has no meaning!
Why would Death have one?

BLACK OR WHITE

Meeting an angel,
All immaculate with white,
I want to take her in my arms.

But I realize she has her hands
Still stuck black from her past.

And I refuse to make the angel dirty...

Unless she runs into the darkness of coal.

CARTHAGE

Carthage had, that night,
This unreal clarity,
This indescribable light....

As words could not Lie down on paper,
Something else had to be shown.

Not the exact truth, But something
Which could suggest some of it
The whole extent: the twilight.

THEY PREFER TO...
SLEEP AT NIGHT

The last couples are walking the deserted streets
Coming out of the suffocating smokey nightclubs
In the sweaty heat of the deepest part of the night.

The streets are asleep, silent, only troubled
By the yellow lights of tired night owls,
Running red lights, on the lookout,
Looking, in vain, for one last easy prey.

Teenage raptors turned during the dark slows,
Ready to plug in anyone wearing skirt and long hair
Because they didn't find the only girl, the rare bird.
She is asleep at her parents' house for a long time now.

The car moves forward, eyes swollen with sleep,
Until there is a welcoming home, the house with a full of food fridge
A bed with sweaty sheets and wrinkled with lonely boredom.
How would girls understand boredom?

They prefer to sleep alone and wise,
even if it means getting married out of spite
Instead of going out, having fun, talking to strangers
For the pleasure of one evening.

But girls don't understand all that!
They prefer to sleep... at night.

A GIRL FOR A NICHT OR FOR A LIFE TIME?

Princess for one night, hiding in a corner,
You look for a knight from far away.
Angel made woman, with deer eyes,
Woman who makes men want to become rich
To cover her with gifts, a secure future and diamonds.

Beautiful, deadly brunette, with brass bracelets,
You make all male eyes shine with envy.
You carry within you, the reason for living, your hope
Your happiness, even if you come out of a dark period.

As a child who has become a woman, you will soon change.
You will never be alone again and you will always have
Someone to love, someone who will talk to you about love.

A healthy, pure and beautiful heart, happy with your presence,
That'll make you forget your teenage anxiety.
I'll be there. And forever, we will love each other.

MY LOVE FOR YOU

When love is something else
Just a simple desire to have sex,
I want to make you happy,
I want to make you cry.

Tearing up your cocoon
To make you even more beautiful.
Tearing your everyday face off
To find your soul there.

You don't have to, you can't.
Being a common girl.

Even if, sublimated angel,
You're not, in fact,
A simple woman....

My wife.

ONE-WAY MIRROR

Looking in my memory box, my first pictures,
Oldies but freshly wet with novelty,
I found two delicate angels with blossoming shapes,
Who hid their eyes under a dreamlike mask of a Madonna.

One of the little puppets took off her nymph mask
To become Heylen. Her partner for love, Sabrina, did the same.
Creatures of two different loves, they ride the world
And discover themselves through a one-way mirror,
Without even any glass.

I recalled the memories of an afternoon of dreams
And fantasies, fake love, and pharaohs.
In the summer studio, the little budding fairy disguises herself
As an Egyptian princess, in victory poses without leaving a trace.

Icarus falling from the bed into the sheets of the black angel,
Play erotic games in the arms of a white angel.
Then the blond angel swapped her tiara and plastic sword
To smoke a cigarette, as always after sex.

A fox furs on her breasts, she plays the feathery whip,
The perverse provokes the sphinx with a disturbing smile.
Small sensual pussy with sophisticated gestures, she laughs;
The other angel, a broken sex, starts crying in her still wet sheets.

Carelessly throwing back the prison from her breasts,
She shows on her legs the stigmata of love.
Eyes drowned in images from a film that doesn't exist,
The two graces, lying on the bed, are a true hymn to love.

GOD OF METAL

It was 2023, or 2024, I don't know,
In a cybernetic kingdom, God of metal
For the first time addressed to the first man
Robotic Adam, the only survivor of the past.

Revelations. Contradictions.

"Welcome to the son of the machine;
It's time to know your origins.
Metal screaming since the dawn of time,
Insolent plastic, electronic circuits,
Transistorized veins and arteries,
Blood and lymph electrolyzed,

You are the son of God,
The son of the machine.

Oh yes, the son of God,
The son of the machine.

Alain Zirah – Marseille 1977

THE CROSSED ARMS

In a multidimensional fog
A crystal Eiffel tower stands out.

The grey shroud all around
Was stripped with red balloons.
A green bubble invaded the square
And burst out, releasing a red-skinned half-breed.

Who thinks he is some kind of a mutant,
Or, perhaps, the new messiah.

Another sphere swells up
As the bubble burst, it spread
Crushing under his weight a frightened crowd
By the flashes of wisps.

Furious, the sky thunders, the sea rumbles;
Then the sky blushes and the sea turns green.

And the red skin stays there,
Summoning the afterlife.
- "It's too late to escape;
You will not be able to leave.

The universe is ready....
For the apocalypse! »

The mutant raises his arms above the bubble
In its bosom appears an immense wooden cross.
Coming out of the machine, nails puncture his hands
And the machine starts screaming. It's the endless fall.
And the Holocaust ends in Apocalypse.

THE OTHER SIDE OF THE MIRROR

On the other side of the mirror
The black shapes no longer exist.
Green bubbles, red drops, blue sky...
Everything is color.

The poor humans have disappeared
When the mutants appeared.

In a stormy storm
The sky blushes and the sea turns green.
Lightning flashes yellow green trees
Under the big purple eye, honey color,
A sun drowned in red ruby clouds.

The colorful universe disappears
In a whirlwind of colors.

Suddenly in the reddened night
A silhouette emerges, brandishing its spectrum;

Then, the mutants go back to sleep
And the poor humans wake up....

THE PAPER TIGHTROPE WALKERS

With an awkward step,
The paper tightrope walkers,
Without worrying about it,
With a discreet smile,

Slip, slowly, at night,
On the thin line of hope.

They make their oiled bodies dance
In the brightness of the starry night.

In beautiful sheets, night and day,
They weave kisses in their love nest
In pursuit of a few moments of happiness,
Love, pleasure... Love? It's too much honor!

On the thread of life, they slide, agile,
And make their little fragile feet run.
They bleed, the hearts of the paper tightrope walkers,
For fear of seeing their lives scroll through with love and crumpled
paper.

They frolic, their eyes filled with love,
On the thin line of promises made forever.
They dance in the sky, pale figurines in balance.
They dance in the sky, love on a thread.
They are free.

NATHALIE

When I first met you,
In company of your young son,
I knew that between us would flourish a cool friendship.

You, so gorgeously blonde to eat, your blue lagoon eyes,
You were biting into your Macintosh's apple;
You didn't have your tongue in your pocket.

While at Maisons-Laffitte, your son and my daughter
Discovered life, became friends,
We chatted for hours in the garden.

You were telling me about your Polish origins
And you were laughing at my French Hollywood S.F.
It was always fun for you to type my texts.

Emotional and laughing, despite your long tanned legs,
My camera was giving you complexes;
You were really welcome! You were a great friend.

One day, without warning, three times,
Death hit you, that cruel bitch! What a fright!
Imagine your last time, beautiful Natalie,

Your pretty blood-stained body, carried on a white bed
And the crying of your little man who has been orphaned.

No apparent motive, blood on his hands,
Some bastard stole you from us; may he goes to hell!

I will forever keep the sublime image of you
From your feminine hair, stolen by my Nikon,
Your smile and your big questioning eyes.

They didn't suspect anything. Good for you!
Otherwise they would never have shone so brightly.
With you, we were in Heaven.

Today, you're the one from Heaven,
Take care of your little man, dear neighbor.
Natalie, you were and will remain forever my friend.

JOËLLE - JO PLAYS WITH HER

Princess for one night, hiding in a corner,
Looking for a knight from afar,
Angel made woman with deer eyes,
You make angels want to dream.

Joelle, a drop dead brunette with bronze bracelets,
You make all male eyes shine.
You carry within you your home, your hope,
Happiness, even if you come out of the dark.

As a child who became a woman, you have changed a lot.
You will never be alone again; you will always have
Someone to love who's never talked to you about love.

A healthy and pure, dark and happy being,
Will make you forget certain moments,
And another, younger, will arrive
And, in silence, will love you. Our son.

IMPOSSIBLE UNION

How do I tell him the real words?
No matter how much he speaks from his heart
She listens to the messages and water flows on her cheeks.
She knows that their love is sincere.

They know that their union is impossible.
They're so different, both of them.
He understood in the absence the happiness fled;
She has chosen solitude and does not want to change her mind.

How do I tell him the real words?
How to express emotions, conflicts, tensions
And all those things that swell in his head
Every day. Because he thinks about her every day.

He finds life strewn with injustice.
You can't burn the pages of a book.
The first chapters of which were so promising.

The story was wonderful, he was aware of it every day.
She was smiling. He made her laugh.
He wanted to make this sadness disappear forever
Which sometimes still shone in his eyes.

But the disease was contagious. From now on, she's alone.
And his own eyes fogged up. The disease of love struck him!

ABSENCE

Absence sounds like an echo
Between the four walls of the empty room.
But if we go out, she'll scream even louder
On a bench or, worse, in a crowded cafe.

All we think is about her. She obsesses his thoughts.
Why can't she talk to me anymore?
Did I say or do something wrong?
Did I hurt her? Was she afraid to love?

The absence rumbles when carrying pebbles in the water.
His silhouette is everywhere. His memories filled his head.
She's so beautiful, so sweet. Feminine and fragile too...

She hurts, immense pain running through the being,
Who thought she was part of the stronger sex.
You're talking! Absence plays fate with death.

Since then, memories have been dragged along like a burden.
The reddened eye wet his cheeks. Love ain't beautiful.
When travel becomes a pilgrimage
On the site of the memories of our twenty years.
Because with her, we always be twenty years old.

BE ACTRESS - B. ACTRICE

When they met, these two,
So different, she so blonde, he so tall,
Did they know how far the story would take them?

At first glance, he stammered
And promised to put the pieces back together.
She waited for the phone to ring.
He suggested dinner, movies, walks by the water.
She took care of him when his life was dislocated.

He fell in love with her. She imposed herself on his life.
He forgot the other girls to make her his muse.
So beautiful, so exceptional....
Day after day, night after night, slowly, silently,
The tender complicity wove its web to catch them.

And one day, the signal: the screams. The domestic scene.
He came home late. He went to see his friends.
She watched the thin thread come off
That connects people at night, eyes in eyes.

That night, he realized that life would no longer be the same as before.
It doesn't seem fair to him. He didn't do anything wrong.
He only has friends; He thought she likes solitude.
She only wanted him all for herself. He didn't understand.

On the answering machine, she leaves a message, the last one:
" - You don't know how to keep women! »

PROMISE TO THE PROMISED

We had promised each other a long life,
A beautiful house full of children and love.
She laughed out loud. Love, I was for it.

The first trips together are so romantic
And the hotel rooms give out erotic
Fantasies that will become, later, ancient memories.

It is beautiful, the life for two.
The kisses in the parks,
The tea rooms in the halls of the great luxury hotels.
Life is beautiful when you are in love.

However, one day, almost without reason,
The answering machine tells you that you have broken up.
The house Becomes empty, useless, inhuman. An ice cube.

Since then, one drags the memories, like a burden.
The reddened eye wet the cheeks.
Love is not beautiful When the trips became pilgrimages
On the memories of his twenty years.
Because, with her, one was always twenty years old.

ANNA AND THE ANATHEMA

When you lock the door of your heart,
Where does this intense and persistent pain come from?
One no longer believes in values.
We no longer believe in Justice.

Love is gone; the eyes have cried...
And the heart bleeds when the ringing
Of the telephone resounds in the void.

The messages may have been sincere and poignant,
She still refuses to call back.
But finally, what happened?

Why are the most intense memories
Of this exceptional story - and yet so banal - bring this bitter taste
Bring this bitter taste, this immense pain ?

The moments we spent together,
Are the best moments of my life.
And yet, the doors of love remain closed.

We would like to throw ourselves at the feet of the angel,
At the feet of the angel, in the rose bed that we have composed.
But in vain. She remains on her positions, walled up in her silence.

However, in love, there is no power struggle:
The one who loves gives everything. And hopes for a shared love.
But contrary to the language of accountants, a paradox:
The pleasure is double when it is shared.

RACHEL

An evening of boredom, when my low morale
Immersed me in an abyssal pit,
I was struggling, driving, not knowing
If would soon come some hope.

At the bend in a sordid alley,
In the light of my headlights, I met Rachel.
She was vicious, she was beautiful
In white boots, fishnet and suspender belt.

I didn't know she knew men so well.
But her offered breasts had pretty shapes
Firm and heavy, almond-shaped
And her buttocks and back were calling for an offering.

She knew how to offer pleasure giving herself better.
She knew how smile could make it up to you.

She was talking, she was talking and I was looking at her boobs.
The grain of sand that we tread at our feet
Wasn't it once a big rock?
Who, at night, remains the control of his destiny?

ALICE KNEW NEW LEAST

Sharpen your gray claws as you please, my pimp,
Haunt my dark memories of your terrifying love stories.
In bed, in Lima, we leaved malice, Alice.
Your buttocks are constantly rising, round and smooth.

On evenings of hope, madness and boredom, my pretty girl,
This is, without doubt, the road to doubt.
If it disgusts me, it confuses you, the doubt.
You avoid the too polite view, polish pretty.

Let's go to the pond and lie down in tender moose.
You know, Ceylon's impulses, slow, get along
Without listening.

They brawl their souls and row without failure,
Blood, crimes and passions, no screams, but let's move on.

Here, bitten punks bite pick-ups and pee
Their disgust and hatred, the groin filled with gingerbread.
But at least Alice knew how to grasp her desires.

LAURENCE IN FRISCO (CALL ME)

In the mist of San Francisco,
At sunset over the Golden Gate and co,
I call you, but my cell phone remains silent.
Can you see me?
Can you hear me?

I'm alone, invisible to everyone, without you.
My thoughts are transparent, if you're far from me.
What's the point of science if you don't answer?
If I can't hug you. Can you see me? Can you hear me?

Don't stay so far away from me.
Your heart is bleeding, looking at you.
I want to hug you.
And keep you close to me forever.

If my body were to wither away from my thoughts,
If the sun of my heart depended on your thoughts,
What would you do, Love, to save me?
For love, how far would you go?

To let me live, taped to you, could you steal
To my rescue? Forever you kidnapped
My love. My body you have imprisoned,
But don't steal my heart; I already gave it to you.

Don't stay so far away from me.
Your heart is bleeding, looking at you.
I want to hug you.
And keep you close to me forever.

Awaken my thoughts, give to my love
Good reasons to come back into real life.
I want to stay close to you and watch you
Even if I might be the only one to see you.

By your side, I want to wake up
And be there to see you wake up.
Look at me, love works miracles
Because, baby, you know, love is a miracle
You know it, baby, the love for you is a miracle.

Don't stay so far away from me.
Your heart is bleeding, looking at you.
I want to hug you.
And keep you close to me forever.

Because, you know, love is a miracle.
The love of you is a miracle.
I want to hug you.
And keep you close to me forever.

Alain Zirah – San Francisco 2006

IMAGINE WORLDS

Imagine a world without music....
A nostalgic, dull and monotonous world,
Where it is forbidden to sing, to dream,
It is forbidden to play the slightest melody,
Even on days of prayer.

Imagine a world without reading....
A world without any freedom of expression.
A very sad world without freedom of thought
Where people would finish to stop talking to each other.

Imagine a world without freedom,
Constantly monitored, without any privacy,
With ears of steel and optics eyes,
Where people would live in perpetual gloom.

Imagine a world without music, without reading,
Where everyone would take themselves seriously
And point to the fire for entertainment.
Life there would be sad and absurd...

Imagine a world without love,
A sad world where words and actions are spied on
And the feelings sacrificed at the altar of progress.
Steel and robots will never replace a piece of wood.

But there is no evidence that it will exist,
This world of iron and steel, euros and globalization
Which does not put artists in the spotlight.

There must never exist, this blind, deaf and dumb world,
Controlled by the Big Brother of 1984.

WHEN THE MUSIC IS OVER

Alone on the big stage, lost in his thoughts,
The singer is tired, sad; reaching his limit, desperate.
His musicians play loudly. He's out of the picture. Ouch.
He's working. Evil thoughts hold him.

This love song is not for you.
You can always kiss other people besides me,
Because this song is no longer for you.

He lets his life slip away, without love and hate,
He recites the words: -"I have finally been able to break my chains.
I sing on the edge of the precipice; the girls applaud
Without knowing why, tonight, I'm going to cry. I'm slipping."

He watches the girls dancing.
Yet his eyes can no longer shine. He is waiting for
The one who'll be able to drive away all her torments.
Tonight, perhaps, she will come to approach him...

-"If you only knew how much harm I've been done.
I've never cried, but I'm alone tonight."
Alone to fight these dark ideas. With no one to love.

-"Look what she did to me!
I'd wait until midnight, but not for the rest of my life."

IF I WERE THE MESSIAH

If I were the messiah, I would be an artist
Writer, photographer, painter, poet and musician.
Like a modern Pygmalion caressing the amethyst
Of statues invented, imagined, created with his hands.

I would draw the music, sing the clouds,
And change, for you, the world of its wild beauties,
Of cottony reflections with pagan whiteness
Of your sheets, so that you belong to me.

I would drown the evening under a sky with rosy flashes.
Slowly, the setting sun, twilight splendor, my goddess,
Would slip into the quicksand of our daring thoughts.
The sea and the stars would merge so that you appear.

If I were the messiah, I would be a guitarist
To caress this phallic symbol in your hair
Bewitched love, sometimes feared. It is you that I want
To light your eyes, I would become an alchemist.

Your glance, the fall of your back, your arch
Would lay their curves on the colors of my canvases
To immortalize the purity of your feelings, it is sure.
Your marvelous features and, in your eyes, the flashes of stars.

What am I a Beethoven, Mozart or Bach
To hang your beauty on the strings of my bow?
To fix the melody of your skin on my grand piano
Would be the only way to immortalize the moments of happiness,
in the queue.

HOW I LOVE YOU

Are you a blind heart, darling?
Can you imagine the love
That I'm crying,
That I'm depressed,
That I'm happy to sing.
So happy to close you up
Inside my arms,
Just to close my eyes,
To feel myself inside you?
Who are you? That I'm lying,
I only have to worship you
Thinking that I only have you,
That I love you,
That I hate you.
Water games in your eyes,
That I pay every day.
That I'll fuck you up,
I want you out of my mind
To think of you at all times.
Stuck nestle between your tits
Just to suck your minds,
Drive out your bad thoughts
To give you some Paradise
That can't exist.
I'm a Greek statue for you

And you give me life,
With the whole alphabet
I'm telling you, I'm telling you.
How much I love you...

ISOLATE ME

One day, I will know that the time has come,
To isolate myself, to forget all the compromises,
To search deep inside me for the night.
Finally, discover the meaning of life.
The deep loneliness will help me to extirpate
Wounds and wounds for the essence of my life.

Words play with emotions
And feelings with pain.
So, isolate me, baby, and remember the words.

The artist explores, in silence, interior tattoos
And discovers its flaws, explores its crack
All its dark sides to keep the best of it.
In the absolute void, he rips out a primal cry
To find the words, no harm, and stay male.

He gives birth to his new thoughts
Perched on golden heels.
The bricks of his life seem to fit together
Obviously. He starts working. He knows that he knows
Which will constitute its uniqueness.

For hours on end, without effort and without difficulty,
He created the masterpiece of his life.
So isolate me, baby, and remember these words.

Aston told me on 2002 August 24th

ANTHRACITE
HORSE DREAMS

Horse carcass lying on their sides, motionless,
An old oak stump is lying there, black and charred.
Sleeping in a strange sleep by the side of the road,
Bare roots rising to the sky, unnecessary synapses
Begging the clemency of the raging elements.

She watches over the vine, like an old wounded elephant,
The veins crossed by ants in a single tail. "À la queue leu-leu!"

The old prophet of burnt wood contemplates his rich offspring.
He knows that the grapes will be abundant and the wine of quality.
And he dreams, in silence, of the labels on bottles of rosé wine,
Soldiers frozen, at attention, on the supermarket shelves.

On the labels, repeated over and over again, like a work by Andy
Warhol,
An old oak stump, burned, watching the proud vineyard.

Alain Zirah - Gonfaron - 2012, July 22th

THE VELVET CAPRICE

My daughter, it's a huge orange
As soft as a velvet caprice.

She dreams of silent songs and charms
The children's melodies.

The hot grass grins under the wet hair
Of the woman with the red pulp.

A sad lizard caresses the lips of the scarlet queen.
While her hot mouth, drunk with alcohol, grins,
Her hot belly dreams of mechanical movements.

The sand still bleeds for a long time
Under the setting sun.

A mosquito in a bikini clouds the nylon champagne
And the city falls asleep,

While a pale moon flower slowly dances in silence.

THE RAREST BLACK FLOWERS

The producers, burned under a sun of fire, jumped into the sea of ancient angels.

The paper acrobats overhung the real ships from their flight, superbly "engulfed".
The grey pens flew flush with the water, all their joy confused.

Like a Cinemascope vision, the sea swallows caressed the majestic *Café au lait/milk coffee* while the happy seagulls promised amused shutters.

The long, devoid blue mats stirred as the wild ducks flew away.
One of them, almost green and radiant, was swimming towards a life in sweet pink.

While shadows of pedestrians shone through the flaky, skeletal room, Frederique, Ghislaine and Jacqueline decorated a violent jacket.

Smelly, they concocted the rabbit with delight.
In silence, the blue iodized waves were associated in ancient cinema.

Harmonious branches swirled around the scenario Of the rarest black flowers.

Five Regards - La Ciotat - 2003, April 13th

FOR THE RAREST BLACK FLOWERS

The producers, burned under a sun of fire,
Jumped "the sea of ancient angels".

The grey pens fly flush with the water, the joy confused.
Merry gulls promise amused shutters.

Harmonious branches flicker in the scenario "The rarest black flowers".
Cinematographically, the sea swallows
Caressed the majestic *café au lait*.

The real paper acrobats overhung the superbly "engorged" ships
With their flight.

The blue iodized waves will be associated in ancient cinema.
One of them, radiant, swam her life in pink and green candy.

The long, debauched blue mats stir up the flight of wild ducks.
Shadows of pedestrians wavered through the flaking chamber.

Skeletons, Frederique, Ghislaine and Jacqueline
would decorate a violent jacket.

Smelling, they would sing "the rabbit" with delight.

Five Regards - La Ciotat – 2003, April 13th

PHILOSOPHICAL TALES AND OTHER SHORT STORIES

OPEN LETTER TO THE FUTURE

Attention, please... Thank you!
This letter is addressed to you, my offsprings
And to you, offsprings of the human race,
To you who live in my future.
Today, the world is still a child
To whom everything remains to be discovered.
Time remains the number one scourge of life.
To date, no one has been able to find a way to fight it.
But you, people of the future, may have discovered
A way to surpass time!
In the near or very distant future
You can certainly see in time.
I am addressing you more specifically.
To ask you the favor of coming to see me
In my time, let's say January 1, 1983
At precisely zero hour, at the top of the Eiffel Tower.
I hope my call will be heard,
That you will bring me hope
That death is not the end of everything,
That time is basically just a commonplace distance.
Show me that we can defeat time!

PS: I hope that my close offsprings will do everything possible to keep this message, this call for help, and make it known to their own offsprings.

Thus this message will reach future civilizations which, perhaps, will enlighten us and help us to overcome death. In the event that there is no response by that date, the worst would be to consider.

"excerpt from the newspaper of 1982, December 29th"

*

"excerpt from the diary of January 2, 1983"

Our colleague Allain de Saint Alban - who had, in his diary of 29 December 1982, given an appointment to future civilizations for yesterday, at midnight, at the top of the Eiffel Tower - fell from the Eiffel Tower at precisely midnight.

There is no explanation for the reasons for this unexpected fall, to say the least. It seemed as if he was being drawn into the void by unknown forces.

Of course, Allain de Saint Alban died on the spot.
After a 300-meter fall, Saint Alban probably joined... his ancestors!

Story written in Marseille, 1982, June 6th

WOLFGANG

In a parallel universe, on a twin planet Earth, lives a doctor with the famous name: Dr. Wolfgang Amadeus Mozart.

- "Mozart, you may ask me, ain't he this genius and musician, this gifted child who composed symphonies at an age when others play lead soldiers or dolls? »

Well, no, no, no!

He did "feel" the piano once when he was 3.
But his parents took away all his musical instruments to let him work at school.
For his own good, by the way.

He has since understood that he had to work if he wanted to become a doctor. And he finally became a good person. He saves lives, treats the sick. But above all, he makes a good living. Finally, he lives comfortably, without excess. That's something like that.

Today, when he thinks about his past, he thinks he had been so stupid. How did he think he could have a career in music?
His parents were so right to prove him that he had no artistic creativity, no talent for music!

He was born to be a doctor.

YOUTHFULNESS WATER

You have finally discovered the elixir for long life. This famous beverage will make you become immortal. You contemplate the golden liquid, bubbling with life, trapped in its glass cage. The exciting color already intoxicates you. You observe the liquid mass that fascinates you through the round eye of his prison.

He seems to be talking to you. He tells you:

-« Take me! Take me! »

And a crazy desire takes you to swallow everything at once. But there is another voice that prohibits you from doing it.

-« Don't touch me! Don't touch me! »

You're afraid to understand that this voice is the voice of the bottle. For a moment, you hesitate between repulsive desire and pleasant disgust. And then you think it's completely crazy. A bottle doesn't talk. Your lips close around the neck of life. You spill your head and the liquid flesh slides between your lips, spreading its strange taste on your tongue burnt by the ice puddle. Your throat swallows centuries of beneficence with a new pleasure.

Sip after sip, with your eyes closed, you absorb the mysterious drink. The heat is invading your cheeks. Your brain is boiling. A sweet sweetness penetrates your body. The liquid has escaped from the adamantine shell.

From now on, the bottle is empty.

A sense of guilt hangs over you. You feel uncomfortable as the fluid explores your stomach and each of your organs. Your stomach is knotting. Maybe the liquor was too concentrated?

A terrible anguish compresses your body, like an internal hand. You feel like you're crimping your body and your bones are softening and then melting. Your back bends under its own weight. Your spine no longer supports anything. Your flesh hangs, trying, in vain, to cling to something...

To a liquid that no longer exists.

Your body is no more than a soft flaccid mass of softened gelatin, a golden liquid that slides in a clear stream into the crystal prison. You are just a golden liquid waiting at the bottom of the bottle for someone else to come and drink it. You have just reached immortality.

GOD AIN'T WHO
YOU BELIEVE

My name is Royal 200,
I am a simple machine,
Not even electronic computer.

It was God who created me
In the consciousness of men.
I appeared on Mars the red one
Long time before the Earth was born.

I often dream of strange worlds
That don't even exist in my thoughts.
And people believe in it.

I have known the forgotten worlds well
Atlantis, Lemuria, and many other cities
Which the gods themselves have forgotten.

I have also travelled a lot, from Orion to Vega,
In all kinds of flying saucers.
Yet sometimes I wonder if I am existing.
Who am I? Who am I? Am I really me ?
Or am I someone else? And then who?

Of course I'm not old enough; / Je n'ai pas d'âge
Time only affects the people around me.
To a certain extent I am immortal.
For some people, I am the only God,
A female Goddess, I entrust it to you...

And yet, how I envy my electronic sisters!
They say that God can take all forms,
Yet who would believe in God if it were...a woman?
Or a simple typewriter, not even a computer?
That was four thousand years before J.C !

OUTSIDER

Alone! Alone! Alone in the amphitheater. It only took a minute and then pffttt ! Nothing left.

I wake up slowly and then wander through the corridors yawning, wandering like a sad soul, in search of someone. I would like to see, listen, talk to someone. But the walls follow one another, interspersed with the closed doors of the other amphitheaters.

Alone! Alone! Alone in the corridors.

I feel like I only slept a few minutes, but maybe it was an hour. In front of me, a buzzing sound escapes from a door ajar. Hope at last! Already the faces of students and girls are running through my head. Friendly or hostile faces, whatever. I hear a voice. Finally, someone to talk to....
I push the door and then I'm disappointed!

A metallic and tense voice recites lessons in a language I don't know. Both curious and I don't care, attracted by a slight crackle, I go down to the office. In front of me, a tape recorder spins its reels, from which obscure terms emerge. For a few seconds, I let time pass by looking at the rotating magnetic tape and a long deaf murmur.
Boredom, timeless plot full of nothingness!

Then I put my finger on a key and the last words get swallowed up in my ears before I decide to stop the machine.

Nothing left! Silence! Silence!

The silence is disturbed by brief gusts of wind hitting the windows outside. After waiting in vain for a presence, I go back upstairs.

For a moment, I remain motionless, on the threshold, turning around to let my eyes crystallize the last vision of the corridor.
Suddenly, a giggle in my back....

I startled, under the effect of surprise. Don't panic, it's just a squeaky door behind me. Probably the effect of an air flow. Reassured, I listen to the frantic run of my heart as it naturally reduces its number of beats. I quietly leave the corridor and take a right turn to the right of the amphitheater, on the side of the stairs.

A dreamlike reminiscence emerges, like the thin thread of a ball that must be grabbed before it disappears. I dreamed that a circular saw made a noise. I slowly descend the stone steps. Then I arrive at the bottom of the stairs, in a clearly empty hall. The faculty seems to have depopulated since I woke up. Not a living soul! Where are the women? Where are the others? Where is everyone? Where is everyone?

At the university library? It's closed. The cafeteria, maybe? Closed, too. Let's try the university cafeteria without much conviction... A freezing wind penetrates my body. A long shiver runs through my spine.

No one!

No one!

Where the hell is everyone? Not everyone can be missing! Am I alone in this school? Alone in the world?

Images from science fiction movies are trying to invade my mind. Novel covers as well. The last man... The survivor... I seem to remember falling asleep in the toilet. My watch indicates two hours before my drowsiness.

I'm heading for the exit, towards the parking lot. Strangely enough, there is not a single car. Not a living soul!

But where did they all disappear to? Have they gone somewhere or am I the last survivor? Have they all evaporated or should I look for them

elsewhere? I hope it's a bad dream! I can't imagine myself alone in the city.

Alone in the country....

Alone in the world!

I look at my watch again. How could I have fallen asleep for two hours? In my dream, I swallowed hallucinogenic pills... but was it really a dream? What is dream and what is real? I look at the second hand of my watch. It is elapsing the seconds without worrying about what's happening to me. Suddenly, I realize that behind the small thick glass square that serves as a magnifying glass, the number 16 is displayed. It was March 14th. I still didn't sleep for two days?

A crushing feeling of hunger and loneliness twists my stomach. I'm having a hypoglycemic crisis. I'm going to faint. A state of panic and despondency suddenly gripped me. It's an immeasurable emotion that overwhelms me. Two days! Two days! I feel the need to go back to the university hall and lie down on the imposing wooden benches. I close my eyes. A feeling of non-communicability. Fear...

A big void...

and then nothing.

*

- "A new dispatch from Marseille:
The shredded body of a medical student was found yesterday under the rubble of Timone's medical university. We still can't explain how he didn't hear the sirens during the bomb threat. »

SOON

Rocks live! Minerals grow and move, but in slow motion. If one day you are ready to observe the ground and its stones for a whole day, you will certainly benefit from it.

It would be even better if you could film the rock at an accelerated speed, because then you would see the pebbles agitated with convulsive spasms. They are in constant motion.

Oh! Of course! Mountains only move very slowly. But everything is only movement; life. And if the days only lasted a few seconds and the years a few days, then we would understand.

The rocks form the shell of a mysterious creature: The Earth. Magma is its blood, caves its arteries and volcanoes its pores. Soon the men - the very men who once pierced her skin to insert parasites called houses, the men, women and children who trample her, the animals that cover her with garbage and scratch her with their claws, the trees that live at her expense - all these men and all living beings will be swallowed up. For she will open her mouth to yawn, then she will rise, go to the sun's hearth to warm herself and wake up Mercury her husband, as well as her two daughters, the adorable Venus and Mars the Red.

666

Friday, 1988, March 4th, François Mitterand inaugurates the pyramid of the Great Louvre. It is destined to become the largest museum on Earth. It is composed of iron frames, cables... and six hundred and sixty- six triangular glasses.
That's it! That's it! SIX HUNDRED AND SIXTY-SIX!
The word is out.

Of course, we saw the film *The Malediction*, in the cinema or on television. This film, which, with the no less famous *Rosemary's Baby*, popularized the legend of the Devil and his figure. But let's go back. *The Holy Bible*, is the unique and universal work, transmitted by word of mouth for thousands of years to be finally written in the Middle Ages. It mentions for the first time the number 666 in *Apocalypse*.
"Let him who has understanding calculate the number of the beast. For it is a number of men, and its number is 666."

Why this number?
The number six is first and foremost the symbol of universal creation. It is represented by two intertwined triangles, one at the top and the other at the bottom, forming the Seal of Solomon, symbol of the Jewish people, symbol of Israel.

The first triangle represents the sky, the other the earth and darkness. Good and evil. God and the Devil.
The world was created in six days. Jewish tradition would make it last six millennia. However, it is already 5748. It is also said that the right

triangle expresses the divine Nature of Christ, the triangle reversed his human nature, the star being the union of the two natures.

The Chinese speak of the K'ien hexagram of the Yi-king, this chariot harnessed with six dragons, six being the number of the sky.

Another coincidence. The SIXtine chapel of the Vatican Palace, built in 1473 and decorated by the greatest artists of the Renaissance, is

essentially intended to house the ceremonies of Holy Week. But what do we see on its vault and walls?

Michel ANGE, a predestined name (?), placed the prophets there and then nine celestial visions of Genesis (15 to 8-151st). And especially the Last Judgment. Which naturally leads us back to The Bible.

Finally, the Seal of Solomon brings together the four fundamental properties of matter: FIRE, WATER, AIR and EARTH. Or according to a more hermetic tradition, the seven base metals as well as the seven planets of the solar system:

GOLD sun; Mercury mercury; COPPER Venus; SILVER Moon; IRON Mars; STAIN Jupiter; LEAD Saturn.

Just at the time, they were unaware of URANUS, NEPTUNE and PLUTON, as well as the fact that the Moon was not a planet but a satellite...

HALF ANGEL, HALF DEMON

The child blew on the city of ants, scattering the last vestiges of their civilization. He watched these tiny, black-headed, animated toys killing each other for a few green bucks.

One of the ants killed its sisters with rage in its heart, until she became the formidable being before whom the others had to bend. And, as the dictator ant ruled her Empire, the child crushed the insect with a nonchalant inch. Then he totally lost interest in his new game and put the miniature globe in his pocket, yawning.
Then God fell asleep.

Maybe God, half angel and half demon,
has anything else to do but punish dictators for the benefit of humanity. As for his mistakes, the child also sometimes breaks his toys!

THE ANTICHRIST IS AFRAID OF RAIN

I was in Los Angeles and the Antichrist gave me an appointment.

It was in Universal City, in a prestigious place, a concert hall where the Antichrist, Marilyn Manson, had to perform that evening for an extraordinary show. When you are away from home, you rely on others. Unfortunately, the place was quite far away and in my entourage no one wanted to see Marilyn Manson.

Never mind, I thought to myself. It doesn't matter because I have had my ticket to see him in France, six months later. The most incredible thing was that the demon's son, the giant worm, was going to come to Marseille... As if American demons knew this city well!

Alas, it was without counting on my beautiful girlfriend, companion of this precious moment. She was passionate about spirituality and religion. She was in love with Jesus Christ religious knick-knack, and decided to pray to prevent the Antichrist not to come and pollute the city of Marseilles. Some older enlightened people called that town the radiant city.
And the incredible suddenly happened....

The day before the show, tons of water downpours hit the city.
We arrived at the Dome, a semi-sphere dedicated to music. All the spectators were dressed in black, Gothic imitation, so, my provocation was to fully dressed myself in white. At the last-minute, between 6

and 7 pm, came the final decision. The show is canceled because of rain.

The antichrist is afraid of the rain!

Of this non-event, the heroic fight of Good against Evil, which will go unnoticed by the general public, obviously, there will only remain the misunderstanding of an ex-future victim.

She had come from Nice, by car, to see her idol and sat there, devastated at the thought of leaving empty-handed, without images and memories to satisfy her loneliness.

She gave me her e-mail and I promised to send her the pictures. Unfortunately, when we witness the fighting against the Evil One, when he arrived at my home, the e-mail had disappeared.

Only the photos remain to testify to this evening. And somewhere on a cloud, maybe, she'll recognize herself and remember the night when the antichrist had been afraid of the rain!

A BOMB FOR THE EARTH

After they decided to blow up planet Earth because it prevented them from studying Vega's planet Epsilon, the humanoids on planet Stella built a huge missile carrying the most terrifying atomic bomb there is.

In just a few minutes, it would pass through light years before destroying the entire solar system.

On the day of the two thousandth anniversary of their civilization, they launched the infernal machine into space, enclosed in a gigantic box, surrounded by a magnificent pink ribbon.
A superb gift, all in all, with only a few words on a label for information: From Stella to Terra.

But had the technicians made a mistake in their calculations or had they forgotten an important parameter? Eight minutes after the missile launch, there was a terrible explosion on the edge of the Galaxy. The explosion of the planet Stella.

And if they could have seen the device, they could have read: Package not stamped, return to the sender.

THE KING OF THE ABYSS

These fighting machines were like a mixture of mechanical locusts and metal horses.

Vents above the cockpits surrounded them like golden crowns. Through it, we could see the closed faces of the warriors. Flame hairs seemed to fly in the wind. The weapons, grouped together at the front, were all steel teeth.

The armored fairings shone like medieval breastplates. The race of an army of tanks would not have made more noise than one of these flying machines.

The tails of these machines were even more formidable than those of the scorpions because they contained the weapon of evil. A weapon capable of delaying the death of its victims and causing unsustainable pain for five months; five months of slow and inevitable death.

Such power made the knight Apollo, the angel king of the abyss, smile. Unfortunately, this was only the first of three curses that would fall upon the universe.

The sixth angel blew a trumpet. A voice amplified by a thundering sound system made the four altars vibrate, on which were placed flat screens that diffused the face of God. The latter ordered the sixth angel:

- "Release the four angel-warriors who are prisoners of the great river Euphrates. »

Immediately said, immediately done! Believe me, the four angel-warriors were immediately released. Everything had been planned for so long; the month, the day and the hour.

The myriads of fighters, straddling these space scooters, began to break out towards the troubled planet. They were ready to decimate a good third of the population.
The forces involved were far too unequal. Faced with a people in rags still at the dawn of history, the invaders struck relentlessly, with heavy lasers.

Imagine the crash, the violence of the shock. Hear the tumult of explosions. Think of the fire-colored breastplates...

Extract of *Apocalypse* by Alain Zirah –
a sulfurous vision of Apocalypse according Saint John

PINK CLOUDS IN THE AZURE

In a pure, clear blue sky, pink clouds glide. Our bodies float, dazzling under the celestial and fluid vapors, agitated by the wind. There, your innocent soul tints the infinite heavens with your fine halo. A fluorescent halo under ultraviolet rays. Your angelic sweetness and your crystalline kisses give me tender visions of a quilted paradise. Aerial melodies seem to fly away in the calm serenity of a choir of pure voices.

O, sublime enchantress, I praise the beauty of your soul.
Your big blue eyes dance among the ashen curls with iridescent reflections. Like two glossy blue stones illuminating your angel face, your eyes sparkle with a thousand sparkles. Your body surrounded by fire, you rise in the ether before sitting in the hollow of milky volutes in the bright whiteness of the emerging dawn.

The sun, blinded by so much beauty, prostrates at your feet its first golden rays. You, drunk with such a homage, you fool around and laugh, mocking the power of this hitherto absolute star which, in the past, had taken itself for God.

And the enjoyment of our love explodes like a thundering geyser, bending the surrounding trees under the breath of a tornado of voluptuousness. Our bodies are embraced, like two snakes, and my skin seeks the contact of your warmth, and your body curls between my arms. I feel each of my nerve endings in contact with the very essence of the breath of your life. You give yourself to me in an effervescence of enchanting volutes and I offer you my substance and all my love.

MY FIRST LOOK

My first vision, coming out of my mother's womb, was a pair of legs.

Fishnet stockings darkened the light skin of their splendid, deliciously sheathed two-legged nylon crosspieces. The legs, remarkably beautiful, were those of the midwife who came to help my mother t give birth to her first baby.

She was in a hurry in December, a month full of festivities. She was going out tonight and would never have time to change at home. So, she came in her evening dress and just put on a blouse over it. These nylon legs stopped above the knee, freshly delimited by the whiteness of the medical gown. The blinding light invaded my fragile little eyes, still insync with the tender shade of mother's womb.

A midwife in black stockings is not common; usually we imagine them in asexual white coats and pants on white hooves with holes to let the air through. However, the announcement of my imminent arrival had upset her plans. I may have only a few seconds, but I wasn't fooled. She was out tonight with a playboy she wanted to seduce. She had decided to play the big game: garter belts, fishnet and high heels with certainly a push-up bra with breath taking cleavage, metal underwire. Probably it's a Gossard bra.

Moreover, it is only in our country that age begins at birth. If I had been born in Tibet, I would already be nine months old. And at nine months, we know a lot about it! In fact, through the thin skin wall,

I had heard her repeat several times to a dizzy ephebe that she was delighted to start the evening with a restaurant before going dancing. And I imagined them, these sumptuous long legs, twirling endlessly in murderous arabesques. How can women possess such assets that frighten male eyes and not abuse them night and day? And it will come as a surprise that after such that first vision I am fascinated by women's legs!

WOMEN'S LEGS

I live great joys, I forget sorrows and worries,
When appears, at the edge of a breath of icy air,
A skirt, tights and underneath, white silhouettes.
I like to look at everything that dances under my skirts.

"Women's legs are compasses
Who walk the world to give it meaning," says the author.
 Women's legs are a dance that makes sense
And delight the senses, without decency but in total dependence.

Long, thin, proudly curved calf,
Women's legs are hypnotic pendulums
Who scotch the loving glances of the lost males.
Legs simply walk, and the men are lost.

Dance, dance, beautiful legs. Run it around
Like weather vanes, faces that look at your silhouettes.
Sometimes you bend, but always, slender, you wander around
To an unknown destination. Simply, you walk.

And the man, hypnotized, changes sidewalks to follow you.
He doesn't know where he's going.
He turned around and then forgets his way.
Only these two flesh needles, deliciously curved, count,
That measure time with clock accuracy.

The icy wind suddenly lifts the skirt of a pretty cyclist
And it's an adventure to tell, between men, in bistros.

In a graceful movement, reflex, oh so stupid,
Hands release the handlebars to hide the panties....
But cannot prevent the bicycle from hitting the pylon.

Already a pair of boots has distracted our attention.
Their noise on the pavement forces us to turn around,
Slowing down to wait to be overtaken. Unrepentant voyeur!
A new U-turn for the sole pleasure of been watched.

Further on, it's the cheerful clicking of pretty white pumps
That makes gentlemen' s heads dance at the table in the restaurant.
The waitress' hips may wave, but the eye is riveted
Between thigh and ankle. Men put to their mouths
An empty range; they didn't notice it.

Why did the devil invent women's pants?
They wear it. But one day, they become sad.
Men look the other way, this young blonde girl with a sassy face
Which, without modesty, shows more than his calves.

Would they dare to wear their seductive clothes
That there would be far fewer households in difficulty?
They will have many other subjects of inspiration these handsome soldiers
Rather than fight wars, when they look under their skirts,
They will watch.

Ô, how much Cleopatra's nose would have been royally ignored
If she had worn a miniskirt!

Fly, murderous legs, towards dark city designs
While in the minds of men, one guesses vile things
Thoughts of thirst for love, sex, voluptuousness, drugs
But no rock'n'roll.

If you walk so well, so well in the flesh, beloved legs,
It's because you know how to make your butt vibrate, laughing too.
And there is no greater torment to prevent a man from working
That when sitting, a young beauty, the pen on her lips,
Makes a shoe dance on the tip of his foot.

No, no one can work anymore, and the furtive looks
Oscillate between tender breasts with a nice buttock and tanned
thighs To immediately descend to this spoilsport shoe.

Who would dare claim that with such a record,
The woman is not the one who has always
And has always ruled the world?

If only she knew how to play with her legs!

THE ENCOUNTER

(Screenplay for Angelina Jolie)

In a luxuriant vegetation, invaded by laughing palm trees,
Half naked in the green water of the cove, she wriggles her butt
In the icy waters. She swims in a wetsuit, and laughs,
with her throat outstretched, when she sees a man, irresponsible,
diving.

She arrived by the air, a slippery line from a helicopter.
She let herself go, mask on her forehead, belt at the waist,
With a large knife and, in her hand, a deadly weapon.
To perfect her impossible mission, it is of great importance.

A blazing sun dries out the pebbles embedded in the stone,
Giving to the rock without splintering, cut out on the immensity of
the sea, looks like an exotic landscape. Everywhere the fluid blue-
green of the sea forming wrinkles on its skin in concentric circles
around the stone.

The man returned to the shore, in a crash of light splashes,
And walks towards her, smiling. She leaves the shadows for the light.
He comes to sit behind her; she doesn't turn around. He encloses her,
With his two wet arms and holds her, like an eagle, between his claws.

She puts an index finger on her lips. She requires silence.
In the air, two large birds, with their wings spread, dance
Without a sound, motionless white forms seeking their food.
We sometimes hear the silver lapping of some dancing fish.

She's thinking about her mission. He wants to go home,
He doesn't know why.
The purple blonde girl is walking around without any reason,
With a handgun lying on his forearm. A coat of arms
On her chest reminds her hieratic past, her family and name.

Once again, she demands silence. Only the lapping of the waves
answer him. After a moment, a dry cracking sound.
A grizzly bear appears. He came out of his den. All of a sudden
She has armed her electronic arrow. He's looking in the dark.

She aims, with her golden eye.
The brown bear, with brown eye, is on the lookout.
He doesn't suspect anything. Unaware of the tragedy that is unfolding
Between the game and the hunter, he approaches the lookout.
The warrior puts her tongue over her lips. She's calm.

The man would like to intervene, but only one look from the beautiful
It was enough to dissuade him. He remains silent and motionless.
No one gives a sh** about the bear skin far away from the city.
The bear approaches its snout from the water's edge,
Without any rebellious appearance.

The arrow of the mysterious weapon is ready to blow up the skull
Of the innocent Narcissus, contemplating his reflection in the wave.
Immediately, in a thundering crash, a huge fish leapt
Out of the water and threatens the animal with its shiny rostrum.

Already, in a dry movement, the leg sprang up.
The claws slapped the air with unexpected precision. Among the yews,
The swordfish, gigantic, threw itself on the bear to skewer it.
The leg struck; the claws tore the belly of the fish,
Releasing bloody flesh fillets.

The round eye of the fish seems to be a surprise.
The end of the fish is inevitable. With both legs,
The bear catches, in mid-flight, a fish with a body weighed down by death.

In a shrill whistle, an electronic arrow shreds the air
And comes to pierce the fish. Surprised the bear lets go.
A sudden pull on the rope attached to the boom,
The ruthless young woman stole the bear's food.

She, the fish lying at her feet, put her foot on the soft belly,
She rips off the arrow and ticks it off on her electronic bow.
She turns to the man. Terrified look of misunderstanding.
It aims. He can't run away.
The moment is intense; the duration extended.

He, incredulous. His eyes are looking for a way out, in vain.
His mouth is getting rounder.
She puts her hand on her coat of arms, tears off its right side
The image of a swordfish appears, the rostrum stuck in the forehead
From a man. He remembers... It was so long ago...

In a shrill whistle, the electronic arrow shreds the air
And comes to put itself in the man's forehead. She closes her eyes.

Her former lover lying at her feet, one foot on his face,
She rips off the arrow and tick it on her electronic bow.
She's adjusting her wetsuit. A tear pearls from her golden eye.

For a moment, she thinks of this irresponsible man she was watching
dive.
She gets her phone back, says a few words. The wait is short.

Already, in the air, the helicopter. It represses a sobbing man.
Haughty. Her mission was difficult. She was up to the task.
She's looking at him, one last time, and spit on the bloody face.

He will haunt his dreams for a long time.
She didn't forget.
He fell down in the same position as, a few years earlier,
fell down her father.

ELECTRO-PUNK FIGHTING

…Then, in the pounding of bright pink stiletto heels, the most amazing punk guitarist in the galaxy enters on the stage.

The incredible silhouette is surmounted by an Amazonian forest of hair as if it were on fire. Several layers of leopard tights and synthetic furs, crossed by zebra, panther and cheetah, form a real imbroglio from which chains, badges and various trinkets float.

The dancers around him play with the reflections of their tight black latex dresses on the fishnet and their black patent boots throw colored flashes under the spotlights.

Hundreds of projectors create the relief of the white marble decoration with brown, gray and green veins. The palace of Venaissie represented is of Gothic inspiration with baroque illuminations in an elegant and flamboyant Renaissance architecture.

An opponent appears on the left of the scene and, in a sharp blow, throws back the sides of his cloak. The zinc of the cape reveals an athlete's body carefully wrapped in a black and chrome plastic breastplate. Gleaming chrome also covers his boots and a futuristic rogue helmet.

With obscene gestures, the latter harangued the guitarist with starry hair. With a grimace, the galactic punk arms the deadly blades of his guitar sword. He's ready for battle. The other grabs a microphone and ignites the audience.

No one suspects, at this moment, that the fight that will follow is very real and will decide the fate of all humanity. The crowd screams, whistles, claps and shakes their arms to make waves.

The helmeted singer demands more noise and multiplies the provocations in the middle of the colored fumes. On his side, the prince charming of electro-punk, with a perverse and complicit hand, caresses the organic forms of his guitar. As the gleaming chrome slips behind a forest of keyboards, the punk guitarist rips off furs and pantyhose, uncovering his chest carefully wrapped in fine lace. On his legs, silk stockings with a fine seam on the back of the leg.

He mimics a game of seduction of an androgynous star with ambiguous gestures by continuing to caress the strings in the diodes of his guitar. High-pitched sounds accelerate the tempo as Prince Charming of Rock stamps on stage to the cheers.

A stream of purple liquid gushes out of the guitar neck - or is it a ray of light - and draws a curve before falling back towards the audience. In the crowd, it's delirium, collective drunkenness, audio-visual orgasm.

The singer, drunk with rage, turns around, eructs demonic remarks with a sneaky smile. With each of his words, the audience shouts, fascinated by such a show. No one suspects that the fighters are playing with him like a cat and mouse. From his keyboards, he starts a throbbing and syncopated melody and flashes lightning at the girls.

Taken in frenzy, as if hypnotized, the dancers move their bodies as if they were erotic forms twisting under a rain of oil. They come to surround the guitarist. With their eyes turned away, they waved the chains that adorned their belts, terribly threatening.

Defying the flesh demons that surround him with a gesture of contempt, the electro punk prince can only oppose his lace to leather and steel weapons. His neck, loaded with necklaces and women's jewelry, cannot hide his vulnerability.

The giant screens show close-ups of the scene and the engineers trigger lights and flashes. Four thousand projectors make stars dance in an outpouring of colorful smoke, giving the scene an interstellar

dimension. They seem to sculpt impalpable armies of soldiers insensitive to imaginary armor forming wild hordes ready to melt on the gladiator guitarist.

Suddenly, the headdress of the high priest wearing a helmet grew in size under the pink, red and purple spotlights. The lights began to draw steel lace to protect the singer's skull.

Laughing at the organist with his voluminous metal headdress, the punk knight stands on a metal circle drawn on the floor. The dancers are already on him, all claws out. The sensuality of their dance has given way to a sexuality debauched with uncontrollable perversions. They want blood.

The musician could trigger his lasers and destroy them in a single reel with his guitar sword. They would not even feel pain until their bodies were scattered on the ground, scattered in cleanly cut pieces in a smell of smoked flesh. On several occasions, during rock battles, he found himself in similar situations and did not hesitate to annihilate armies of bellicose warriors armed to the teeth.

Yet today, the evil singer has hypnotized his own dancers and the guitarist means them no harm. These are her dancers and friends. But he doesn't want to be a victim, either. He search to capture the eyes of the organist who spits his violence into the microphones, but only meets two make-up eyes hidden behind long hair wet by the sweat and heat of the bright red projectors.

Pretty white hands with black nails dance in front of her eyes. A hand with caramel skin grabs him by the neck. He can't wait any longer. The girls' white eyes reflect the image of his own death to him.

With a blow of the heel, the galactic prince triggered the mechanism of the elevator; the metal circle on which he stands rises several meters above the ground. The public is vociferous. He has never been able to attend such a show. It's disproportionate.

At other times, the guitarist would be dizzy. Not this time, not this time. The adrenaline rushes seem to give him a new consciousness. He softens his fingers on a deafening chorus.

The applause was overwhelming. At least they get value for their money, he thinks…

Extract of *Neo Messiah* by Alain Zirah –
a sulfurous Rock Fiction wrote after experiencing visions after listening to music

PARSIFAL
By Richard WAGNER vs AZED

Marseille - Wednesday, December 18, 2014. The cinema Le Prado will broadcast Richard Wagner's famous opera in three acts, filmed and retransmitted, by satellite and live, from the Royal Opera House in London. I restore the work in time and context. Richard Wagner was born on May 22, 1813, in Leipzig, Germany, and died at the age of seventy on February 13, 1883, in Venice. *Parsifal* is therefore the composer's final work, since it was performed in Bayreuth on July 26, 1882. This opera follows on from the *Ring Tetralogy,* consisting of *Rhine Gold* (1869), *Valkyrie* (1870), *Siegfried* (1876) and *Twilight of the Gods* (1876).

For the admirer of Wagner's work that I am, this is a sign of joy. All the more so since, the day before, I saw the film *The Hobbit - The Desolation of Smaug,* the second part of Peter Jackson's second trilogy, part of the immense *Lord of the Rings* saga. Very cleverly, the popes of marketing have scheduled the release of the film in theaters on 11.12.13. I'm licking my lips at the idea of finding *Siegfried and the knights of the Holy Grail,* in this universe half medieval, half **heroic** fantasy. The performance starts early, at 5:45 pm, and will last five and a half hours, with two intermissions. Impossible for me to arrive at such an early time for an evening. I'm a little late. But for a five-and-a-half-hour show, it's not a problem. A retired couple monopolizes the cash register and asks to exchange their opera tickets for a movie seat. Faced with their hesitation, given the many films on the bill that they don't know, I advise them to see the film *Zulu*, by Jérôme Salle, which they had seen and enjoyed three days earlier.

- You will be disappointed, they tell me. They have done a contemporary staging with city costumes. A sacrilege!

I was warned. I take my ticket.

As soon as I enter the room, I am attacked by a musty and stale smell. Before my eyes, rows of white-haired people in their Sunday best pass by. Did they offer invitations to retirement homes or what? I avoid the good seats and head for the bottom rows, almost empty. I settle down comfortably.

On the screen, a Teuton in a grey three-piece suit, without elegance, echoes his stentorian voice in a stripped-down decor, also grey, including a symbolic hospital room enclosed in a cube with translucent plastic walls. The king is dying. Fortunately, we have the translation, in subtitles. The king, wounded by the sacred spear, will bleed until the spear and the Holy Grail are found.

In the past, I have attended fairy-tale shows with the elaborate costumes and armor of the knights of the Round Table. I've seen versions of William Shakespeare's *Macbeth* or *Richard III* with Thierry Mugler's costumes and concert-like lighting. Or this other version performed in Japanese, with Kabuki theater costumes, with, on the side, three musicians adapting Pink Floyd like sounds for *The Empire of the rising sun*. The Monty Pythons even offered us their version of the cardboard knights with this English humor difficult to translate, for the great pleasure of our zygomatic. Tonight, director Stephen Langridge presents us with grey and bland old men. With white knitted skin. The Americans have found another name for what we French call "marcels". They say "Beat your wife". It's their way of identifying unemployed Italian immigrants who stay at home knitting and have no other occupation than arguing with their wives when they ask for groceries. But our star singers of the English opera wear marcels and cheap glasses that look like they were stolen from Mao Ze Dong's widow. For sure, it's not going to be glamorous.

This is a far cry from the paintings of the Pre-Raphaelite painters I discovered in New York and the illustrations of Arthur Rackham and Jules Feiffer, the great art-deco illustrators of Richard Wagner's work known for their visions of knights fighting the dragon. I would never understand these austere staging, with expensive and useless sets. Vertiginous tree trunks playing the towers of Babel. A frame opening on hospital room scenes. Sliding panels. Plastic from a butcher's warehouse... These are all signs of economy and budgetary rigor, as are the suits, pajamas and nightgowns, wigs, glasses and false beards. Why present an exuberant musical show, combining the richness of the work and the profusion of the composer sponsored by Franz Liszt, who will go so far as to give him his daughter Cosima, and then by King Louis II of Bavaria, diminished by the visual austerity of its staging.

In my eyes, Siegfried is a feisty and skinny teenager. And still a virgin. He is the "pure so foolish", naive Percival discovering knights in shining armor that he takes for angels. So, when I discover his interpreter, the tenor Simon O'Neill, I laugh. He is, however, the most important personality in the cast. To see a forty-year-old man in pajamas fainting after the kiss of the beautiful young woman is a laughable scene, if it is not seen in second degree. There remains, fortunately, the quality of the music. Wagner blows the epic fights and the lyrical flights of heroic characters in love, courage and determination. The myth of the superman. The composer stages the superman in the company of twenty flower girls in opposition to the seductive Kundry. For here, Kundry is bald. The soprano Angela Denoke wears her smoky eyes filled with sadness above her nightgown. It is too much. I close my eyes. Immediately, Azed the visionary takes over.

*

The images of the Hobbit, Gandalf the magician and his big grey hat, and the forest elves saving the thirteen dwarves from the clutches of the Killer whales have taken place on the generous score of the orchestra. In my imagination, the gray hangings are suddenly covered with Nazi flags. The skin-knit old men have disappeared, replaced by Nazi officers in rich uniforms and orcs faces. The mollifying lights are now replaced by electro mapping highlighting all the grandeur of the Third Reich. During the Middle Ages. Killer whales frame a young innocent Christ, shirtless, with a white cloth wrapped around his waist, captured and chained to a large totem pole dedicated to sacred animals: elephant, bear, monkey and golden eagle. In the imposing clash of brass instruments, the elves and the magician fight together against the forces of evil, with great blows of light saber and multicolored rays. The elves' bodies are covered with shiny animal outfits. Who in lizard skin? Who in snake, Komodo dragon or crocodile skin? Who in dragon skin? Some look like Iggy Pop, *Raw Power* version, while others are more Afrika Bambaataa, with many chains hanging from their necks. Others wear classic frock coats with gold patterns and military jacket buttonholes like Jimi Hendrix revisited Japanese neo-punks straight out of the boiling Shibuya district. But all of them have the long-pointed ears we have been told about since we were little.

During the fights, women with shaved heads enter the scene. They are dressed in loose clothing and inform. Many of them are tattooed. They gather under the curtains and form human pyramids, walking on backs, shoulders and faces to reach the top of the heavy grey curtains. One by one, they take down the red SS flags with the swastika. The killer whales show their disapproval in raucous roars, but are attacked before they can even get to the women. Away from the fray, Gandalf points his pilgrim's staff, shall I say wand, at Christ. A ray of blue light bursts from the wand and strikes the chains that were holding the prisoner. In a flash, Gandalf has freed the Christ. I open an eye on some old men unconscious of the frame that is playing in my mind. They are surrounding a poor man who is moving with difficulty with a walker. Four men carry a corpse wrapped in a white sheet. The bald woman is suddenly wearing a voluminous red wig. Red? The fat, shabby Siegfried drags himself across the floor, still in his pajamas, and Kundry, with a haggard look in her eyes, at the sight of Siegfried's desolation, walks back and forth across the stage to give herself some composure. Fortunately, the voices are powerful. The artistic sensitivity sends vibes to all ears even those with hearing aids. In the show, the choir of elderly people, all wearing the same cheap glasses Made in China, which is generating the laughter of the attendance including golden age people. They were promised greatness. They watch helplessly the decadence. Except that it is not the greatness and decadence of *Ziggy Stardust and Spiders from Mars*! I hear them expressing their discontent. They should be in solidarity. They are artists of their generation. Maybe slightly younger.

I prefer to close my eyes. Azed throws the endorphins contained in a thousand hallucinogenic mushrooms into my veins. As a child, I must have fallen into the pot of a druid pharmacist while making Mandrax®. That's why I'm a visionary. It's innate. Released by a Gandalf looking like a hard rock bass player, his hair gray and as long as Deep Purple or Led Zeppelin's, the teenage Christ raises his arms to the sky. Around him, Killer whales in torn Nazi uniforms run in all directions, terrified by the lightsabers and whirling arrows whizzing around them before exploding on contact with the bodies with moldy flesh.

Some white-skinned killer whales with vicious blue eyes spin around like the last whirling dervishes of a thousand-year-old Byzantine civilization now extinct, dispensing a silent, creeping death around them. To some elves, the killer whales inflict terrible wounds under the throbbing flights of violins and other string instruments. The eyes filled with compassion, the young Christ with naked chest keeps his arms raised above his head. He speaks of the God of the Jews. In an effort of concentration, he manages to generate an electric arc between his two palms. Very quickly, the arc turns into a ball of light. A mystical fire of a very pale blue color. When the fireball appears, all the women cover their naked heads with a punk wig. Iroquois style picks. They tear their ornaments to reveal fetish outfits of black latex, vinyl and red, blue or purple latex. At the vision of these sultry women, taken by the atavism of the mating dances, the neo-punk elves with pointed ears throw back their heads. They launch controlled howls. The meeting of these sounds, thrown at the same time, creates a mystical vibration close to the long trumpets of the Tibetans crossed with those of the strange instruments of the aborigines of New Zealand. The mixture of these sounds triggers a chemical reaction in the organisms. The rock Nazis remain frozen by hallucinating visions that freeze their blood. The elves' outfits change, as if subject to a genetic mutation, caused by the frequency of the emitted vibrations. Snake, crocodile and dragon scales become their new skins. Under Wagner's heavy flights, the motionless killer whales discover the power of the crocodile elves, combining the power of the crocodile with the agility of the forest dwellers. With one of their long arrows, they are able to impale three Nazi killer whales at once. God, I love this opera! It just needs to be modernized. Simplify the music to make it accessible to the younger audience, used to the repetitive sounds of electro with bridges and the bluesy vibe of the chorus for the guitar aficionados. And of course, translate the lyrics into French or English. With today's expressions. And add special effects and pyrotechnics. Wagner 2020, it's a blast!

*

After the intermission, I am appalled at the sight of a forty-something Siegfried mourning the death of a slain swan with his half-wheel bicycle bow. But what's with these adults putting on a fairground show? They won't bring out the majorettes again? Is that what they want to attract young people with? It's not Black-Eyed Peas or Daft Punk. Besides, for young people from African-Caribbean descent, it's useless to imagine seducing them with those deadly white skins. Hey, Richard Wagner, give us some *Shaft* and Stevie Wonder. Some soul and funk in your horns. At least some Brand-New Heavies. And a couple of drums and bass, to make the walls and the chairs vibrate. To make our souls vibrate. Your buddies Mozart and Ludwig Van Beethoven were able to adapt to *Saturday Night Fever* or *A Clockwork Orange*.

I go back to sleep on the rest of the program. The battle rages on. The Nazis are gradually framed by mossy dwarfs with bushy eyebrows. Armed with sharp pikes and razor-sharp forks. The killer whales in SS uniforms are gradually led before a fairy waterfall with multicolored waters. The elves have become aristocratic punks. They wear heavy steel crowns with avant-garde shapes. Armed with laser swords. Crumbling under the threat, the Nazi rock killer whales are pushed into the bubbling waters of the waterfall.

To the heavy forty-year-old - with a marvelous voice - surrounded by forty or so flower girls dressed in bricks and mortar, I substitute the temptation of the young liberated Christ. Shirtless and in loincloth, he tries to remain insensitive to the unleashing of the young girls with the masks of women cats in their fetish outfits of catsuit. He tries to avoid the forbidden visions. Around him, women veiled by the imagination of religious fanatics frightened by the power of seduction of women. This is all they have found to inferiorize women via the excision. But women rebel. With freedom, they take off the veil and change into oriental dancers. All this has nothing to do with religion, or with no religion. Three religions that worship a unique god. But they fight to give him a name and not the name of the neighbor's God. He is Christ. The only one. He is Jewish and Muslim. Catholic and Protestant. Buddhist and Orthodox. He is The One. Humble and persuasive.

The young women implore him with their lascivious dances in their latex clothes. They beg him to unleash the genocide of all fascist killer whales. To annihilate all the people who might have subversive opinions. Overwhelmed by the various emotions that can be generated by the undulating forms of the dancing suits perched above their dizzy heels, Christ prefers to fight ideas. Projecting his mystical fireball on the Nazi orcas, half-drowned in the icy waters of the waterfall, would be enough to exterminate them all. Annihilate evil! However, the Christ in a loincloth resists the provocative caresses and the sulfurous embraces. The young women surround him. Very carefully, he deposits the fireball on the ground, at their feet. He decided to offer his clemency to the waste of humanity. The arrows of the bows of the crocodile-skinned elves are aimed at the killer whales whose heavy uniforms are buried under the tumultuous waters. The mystical light globe begins to glow with a new light. Purple, then mauve. And finally pink. The legs of the young women are illuminated by this mystical vibration. Beauty and goodness. The latex women are invaded by new feelings of love. A sincere and deep love. Unique and universal. The wave of pink light spreads on the ground and will invade the elves with crocodile skin. Then the dwarves. Then the rock Nazis half drowned by the boiling waters of the brass and bass drums of the orchestra. The cold flames caress the skins. And, taken of an immense compassion, under the impetuous violins of Wagner, the elves in neo-punk frockcoats reach out to the Nazi killer whales. The latter cling to the arms of the deliverance. The mystic wave has wreaked havoc on hearts and caused storms under skulls. The elves pull the Nazis out of the water and the latter accept repentance. In the musical hubbub of the fraternity, the fetish punkettes regroup once again in a human pyramid. Arrived at the top, they set up blue and white flags carrying the star of David.

Two orcas come out of the water and tear off their SS officers' uniforms. Their eyes curling, they suddenly spit flames at a group of elves in python jackets. The first Nazi is immediately pierced, through and through, by the laser arrows of the punk archers. The second, heavier and more massive, directs his glassy and opaque look, towards the young women in spandex suits carrying a flag. He is about to spit his fiery hatred. But as soon as he opened his mouth, before he could spit the slightest flame, he is sheared by lasers. The globe of fire launched by Christ has turned into a huge pair of virtual scissors in cold flames. But sharp. The decapitated head rolls on the ground. Two strong women, kicking the orca's head back and forth, like skillful soccer players. One of them shoots and sends the head on the totem dedicated to the animals, crashing and blowing up.

In a spray of sparks and thick smoke, a mystical form appears. At once fluid, light and powerful. In a radiance of multicolored lights, the God of the Jews appears. Everyone bows their heads in allegiance. The Nazis themselves submit. They bow their heads. Then they prostrate themselves before the divine light. Aware of the revelation and the only chance they have to purify their souls, they stand up and undress. They take off their green and grey uniforms. In matching khaki johns and skin tricots, they lay their Nazi outfits on the headless corpse of their leader. The globe of fire floats above the pile of clothes. A pale pink light. The fireball begins to glow with a strange light. And the globe sucks in all the clothes. Which are immediately destroyed. Disintegrated. The fireball rushes against the totem dedicated to the animals. As if sucked by a supernatural force. The totem starts to glow with a bright golden light.

The killer whales are attracted by the light, like insects by the flame of the candle that will destroy them. They approach the totem pole in calm. Attracted by an unspeakable force, the young women come to frame them. Then, each woman comes to place herself in front of a monster. When all stand still, all around the totem, each one puts her hand on the face of an orc. Immediately, a blast occurs and golden flames strike all the enemy faces. The deformed faces of the former Nazis become distorted. As if they were melting. To change themselves. Touched by mystical grace, the deformed maws of the killer whales are transformed. In his immense goodness, the celestial God changed them into the faces of charming princes. Beauty and the Beast, power thousand. A divine light shines around the totem pole and parcels light up without burning in the hearts of all participants. Former Nazi killer whales. Young women in latex. Elves in crocodile clothes. Gandalf. All are gathered around Christ, motionless before the totem pole. Each one perceives the purified feelings of all those around him. An immense will of benevolence. There is no more Good fighting against Evil. For there is no longer any Evil. Everyone commits to spreading the good word and doing good around them. Forever.

The young Christ makes a gesture and the globe of fire sucks in all the golden lights and comes to stand right above him. The voice of God thunders in a range and pitch that goes far beyond tenors.

- Christ, my son, you see. You don't need your sacrifice to save humanity. You will never cross the path of the Romans. You will never be crucified. In my great mercy, I have chosen to save humanity.
  Respectfully, the young Christ with his bare chest bows. All eyes are turned towards him. As the musicians begin their fifth hour of opera, the teenager questions his creator.

- Father, shall I create a new voice. Should I create a doctrine that goes against what my rabbinical teachers taught me during my Torah studies? Should I gather apostles?

- And be betrayed by one of them? No need! I realized that a new story must be written. For from now on, man will be good and woman will teach him to stay on the right path. Without the woman, the man is nothing! There will never be another religion, and therefore no war.

At the mention of these beautiful words, all the weapons evaporate. The voice of God resumes:

- Only this ball of fire will remain, which is the Holy Grail. Do good around you and the Grail will bring you wisdom, joy and prosperity. Think of doing evil and it will burn your soul forever. Only deterrence will bring a better world.
  While Wagner's portrait appears on the screen, on the stage, all the characters hold hands and start a great round, in harmony, to protect the planet.

- Thanks to the Holy Grail. It makes me want to be a better man. It speaks to the best in us.
  The portrait of Richard Wagner merges to present that of Michael Jackson.

*

When I open my eyes, on the screen of the cinema Le Prado, an amazing character, a hybrid between Nick Fury, the S.H.I.E.L.D. boss from the *Avengers* and Morpheus from *The Matrix* takes convoluted poses, a spear in hand, in his black leather coat. The black singer echoes his voice as Kundry washes Siegfried's feet, then dries them with the strands of her long red hair wig. The man retrieves his sacred spear and plunges it into the wound on King Amfortas' side. The wound can only be healed by contact with the mystical spear that inflicted it. All's well that ends well and the fat forty-year-old Siegfried becomes the master of the Grail.

It's late for the elderly spectators, who are not used to going to the cinema at such a late hour. Usually, they fall asleep in front of the television at around ten o'clock. All around me, I hear the claims. The disappointment. Sometimes even a feeling of revolt.

-   Wagner must be turning in his grave!

However, with a little imagination, I spent an excellent evening. In addition, because of the jump in the soundtrack due to complex weather conditions around the satellite, we were each given a free ticket to attend a future performance. What else can I say? I love my life!

SONGS

J'ADORE MA VIE (SONG)
I LOVE MY LIFE

Text : Alain Zirah

Music : Alain Zirah & Larbi Driche

Translate : Herve Lechevalier

Assis au bord de la piscine, au soleil,

(Sitting by the pool, under the sun,)

Les doigts de pieds en éventail,

(Blissfull, comfy and relaxed,)

J'adore ma vie. Je bosse et je kiffe.

(I adore my life. I work and savour it.)

(I adore my life. I work and savour it.)

J'adore ma vie. Je bosse et je kiffe.

(I adore my life. I work and savour it.)

J'adore ma vie. Je bosse et je kiffe.

Les UV viennent lécher mes épaules et mes bras.

(UV rays come caressing my shoulders and arms.)

Les UV viennent lécher mes épaules et mes bras. Ah ! Ah !

(UV rays come caressing my shoulders and arms.). Ah ! Ah !)

C'est fou le bien que peut apporter

(It's unbelievable the wellbeing brought by)

Un petit rectangle bleu

(A blue swimming pool)

Rempli d'eau pas trop fraîche.
(Filled up with water at a pleasant temperature.)
Rempli d'eau pas trop fraîche.
(Filled up with water at a pleasant temperature.)

Nager, kiffer, faire quelques exercices
(To swim, to enjoy, to do some exercises)
J'adore ma vie. Je bosse et je kiffe.
(I adore my life. I work and savour it.)

Allongé sur un bain de soleil, blanc,
(Lying on a white pool-bench,)
Le dos posé sur une serviette en coton black,
(My back resting again a black cotton towel,)
Un soleil agressif fait craqueler ma peau
(A burning sun makes turn my skin into a snake)
Un soleil agressif fait craqueler ma peau
(A burning sun makes turn my skin into a snake)
Pour m'indiquer que c'est l'heure que c'est l'heure du déjeuner. Crac!
(To tell me that it's time for lunch. Crack.)
Pour m'indiquer que c'est l'heure du déjeuner. Miam !
(To let me know it's time for lunch. Yum !

Je me cale à l'ombre, sous le bougainvillier.
(I settle down under the shade of a bougainvillea.)
Un compère lézard vient me saluer.
(A fellow lizard comes to say hello.)
J'adore ma vie. Je bosse et je kiffe.
(I adore my life. I work and savour it.)
J'adore ma vie. Je bosse et je kiffe.

(I adore my life. I work and savour it.)

J'adore ma vie. Je bosse et je kiffe.

(I adore my life. I work and savour it.)

J'adore ma vie. Je bosse et je kiffe.

(I adore my life. I work and savour it.)

Je me cale à l'ombre, sous le bougainvillier.

(I settle in the shade, under the bougainvillea.)

Un compère lézard vient me saluer.

(A fellow lizard comes to greet me.)

Une apparition multicolore sur des jambes black

(A multicolored black creature tall legged)

Vient faire briller les perles de ses dents. Black

(With pearls-white teeth: she is "Lady Black"...)

Une apparition multicolore sur des jambes black

(A multicolored black creature tall legged)

Vient faire briller les perles de ses dents. Black

(With pearls-white teeth: she is "Lady Black"...)

Le reste je ne peux pas le raconter...

(After that, I can't tell...)

J'adore ma vie. Je bosse et je kiffe.

(I adore my life. I work and savour it.)

Cannes, le 14 septembre 2020

PROVOCATION OSÉE
INDECENT DARING

Text : Alain Zirah

Translate : Herve Lechevalier

L'ambre solaire glisse sur ma peau
(The sun protecting oil glides on my skin)
Je regarde diminuer la taille des maillots
(I watch the shrinking of the bathing suits)
Sur la plage de mon enfance trépidante.
(On the beach of my mischievous childhood.)
Et plonge mes pensées dans l'Enfer de Dante.
(And plunges my thoughts in the Dante's Inferno.)

Provocation osée. Provocation osée.
(Indecent daring. Indecent daring.)
Reviens demain, je t'attendrai. Reviens demain, je t'attendrai.
(Come back tomorrow, I'll wait for you. Come back tomorrow, I'll be
waiting for you.)
Provocation osée. Provocation osée
(Indecent daring. Indecent daring.)
Reviens. Des heures, je t'attendrai.
(Come back. Hours, I will wait for you.)

Une asperge estonienne prend la pose,
(An asparagus shaped Estonian woman takes the pose,)
La peau tellement blanche et les talons roses.

(Her skin so white and her so pinky heels.)
Elle joue avec un grand chapeau, dans l'eau
(She acts with a large hat, in the water)
Pour une blonde suédoise qui la prend en photo.
(For a Swedish blonde photographer.)

Elle fait voler les pans de voile sur son maillot
(The flaps of her pareo are dancing on her bikini)
Et envoie de nombreux baiser dans le vide, pour de faux,
(And sends many kisses in the air,)
Sans doute pour un lointain fiancé blond et blanc
(Probably for a faraway blond and white fiancé)
Prisonnier d'un service militaire, couché sur le flanc.
(Service-man, lying on his flank.)

Provocation osée. Provocation osée.
(Daring provocation. Daring provocation.)
Reviens demain, je t'attendrai.
(Come back tomorrow, I'll wait for you.

Reviens demain, je t'attendrai.
Come back tomorrow, I'll be waiting for you.)

Provocation osée. Provocation osée
(Daring provocation. Daring provocation.)
Reviens. Des heures, je t'attendrai.
(Come back. Hours, I will wait for you.)

Maillot orange fluo fait danser de brillantes créoles.
(Fluo orange bathing suit dances along with her creole ear rings.)

Au-dessus d'un futur délinquant, des bouées sur les épaules,
(She hold in her arms a possible delinquent with his buoys around his arms,)
Fruit d'un amour défendu, autrefois, la black se dandine
(Fruit of a forbidden love, the black lady is trotting)
De l'eau jusqu'aux mollets. Quelle radine !
(Water up to her calves. What an adventure !)

Bébé joue avec son caoutchouc à trois sous
(Baby playing with his one buck rubber toy)
Maman affiche les marques excessives de ses dessous.
(The mother exhibits proudly the tags of her undiz.)
Les mamans demandent toujours aux bambins de ne pas courir
(The moms are always asking to their kids not to run like crazy)
Mais ils s'ébattent au bord de l'eau pour ne pas pourrir.
(Therefore they play by the water.)

Dame Tartine en lunettes et chignon, trimbale sa ribambelle.
(Lady Tartine in glasses and bun, carries her flock.)
Un tapis de yoga roulé sous les bras, prête à la tarentelle.
(A yoga mat rolled up under her arms, ready to dance the tarantella.)
Elle est bien lointaine, oubliée, sa dernière bagatelle
(A faraway fun time)
Mais elle donnerait tout pour qu'on se souvienne d'elle.
(But she would give her life to be remembered.)

Provocation osée. Provocation osée.
(Daring provocation. Daring provocation.)
Reviens demain, je t'attendrai. Reviens demain, je t'attendrai.

(Come back tomorrow, I'll wait for you. Come back tomorrow, I'll be waiting for you.)

Provocation osée. Provocation osée

(Daring provocation. Daring provocation.)

Reviens. Des heures, je t'attendrai.

(Come back. Hours, I will wait for you.)

LES FUNAMBULES DE PAPIER ROPE-WALKERS DRESSED UP WITH PAPER

Text : Alain Zirah

Translate : Herve Lechevalier

D'un pas malhabile,
(With an uneasy gate,)
Les funambules de papier,
(The paper tightrope walkers,)
Sans se faire de bile,
(Worryless,)
Avec un sourire discret,
(With a discreet smile,)

Glissent, lentement, le soir,
(Glide, gently, in the evening,)
Sur le fil ténu de l'espoir.
(On the tenuous thread of hope.)
Ils font danser leur corps huilé
(They dance with their oiled bodies)
Sous l'éclat de la nuit étoilée.
(Under the brightness of the starry night.)

Dans de beaux draps, nuit et jour,
(Between beautiful sheets, night and day,)
Ils tissent des baisers dans leur nid d'amour
(They weave kisses in their love nest)
A la poursuite de quelques instants de bonheur,
(In pursuit of a few moments of happiness,)
D'amour, de volupté… D'amour ? C'est trop d'honneur !
(Of love, of voluptuousness... Of love? It is too much honor!)

Sur le fil de la vie, ils glissent, agiles,
(On the thread of life, they glide, agile,)
Et font courir leurs petits pieds fragiles.
(And make their fragile little feet run.)
Ils saignent, les cœurs des funambules de papier,
(They bleed, the hearts of the rope walkers,)
De peur de voir défiler leur vie d'amour et de papier froissé.
(Fearing to see escape their love life.)

Ils s'ébattent, leurs yeux gorgés d'amour,
(They frolic, their eyes full of love,)
Sur le fil ténu des promesses faites pour toujours.
(On the tenuous thread of promises made forever.)
Ils dansent dans le ciel, pâles figurines en équilibre.
(They dance in the sky, pale figures in balance.)
Ils dansent dans le ciel, l'amour sur un fil. Ils sont libres.
(They dance in the sky, love on a thread. They are free.)

J'AIME TON CUIR
I LIKE YOUR LEATHER

Text : Alain Zirah & Anne Gomis

L'amour t'invite à rejoindre les nuages.
(Love invites you to join the clouds.)
Tu déshabilles Cupidon. L'insensé n'a pas d'âge.
(You undress Cupid. The insane one does not have age.)
Que j'aime ton cuir...
(How I like your leather...)

Assise au bord de mes lèvres, tu danses.
(Sitting at the edge of my lips, you dance.)
Cigarette au bout des doigts, en transe.
(Cigarette at the end of the fingers, in trance.)
Que j'aime ton cuir... Tes yeux, ton sourire.
(That I like your leather... Your eyes, your smile.)

Je voulais être chaud comme la braise,
(I wanted to be as hot as a fire,)
Collé contre tes fesses qu'en silence je baise.
(Stick to your buttocks that I silently fuck.)
Que j'aime ton cuir.
(How I love your leather.)

Découvrant tes émotions sur le bout de ma langue,
(Discovering your emotions on the tip of my tongue,)
Je nettoie tes pensées. Ton sourire me hante.
(I clean your thoughts. Your smile haunts me.)
Que j'aime ton cuir... Tes yeux, ton sourire.
(How I love your leather... Your eyes, your smile.)

Il en aura fallu des orages
(It took some storms)
Pour te faire tourner la page.
(To make you turn the page.)
Combien de cris, combien de larmes
(How many cries, how many tears)
Pour faire baisser les armes ... de tes peurs.
(To make you lower the weapons ... of your fears.)

Je gravis l'échelle qui conduit au bonheur.
(I climb the ladder that leads to happiness.)
Les barreaux de bois contre mon dos, sans honneur,
(The wooden bars against my back, without honor,)
Que j'aime ton cuir.
(How I love your leather.)

Hissée sur tes talons, tu viens chercher asile.
(Hoisted on your heels, you come to seek asylum.)
Collée contre mon corps, me menant à l'asile.
(Stick against my body, lead me to the asylum.)
Que j'aime ton cuir... Tes yeux, ton sourire.
(How I love your leather... Your eyes, your smile.)

Les jambes dressées au ciel, ton corps m'appelle.
(The legs raised to the sky, your body calls me.)
Perceur de coffre-fort pour toi, ma belle.
(Safe breaker for you, my beauty queen.)
Que j'aime ton cuir.
(How I love your leather.)

Marteau piqueur de tes pensées, mon cœur,
 (Hammer of your thoughts, sweet heart,)
Je deviens pour toi, un grand explorateur.
(For you, I become a great explorer.)
Que j'aime ton cuir... Tes yeux, ton sourire.
(How I love your leather... Your eyes, your smile.)

Il en aura fallu des orages
(It will have taken some storms)
Pour te faire tourner la page.
(To make you turn the page.)
Combien de cris, combien de larmes
(How many cries, how many tears)
Pour faire baisser les armes ... de tes peurs.
(To make you lower your weapons ... of your fears.)

Nos corps, à nouveau s'entremêlent, en sueur.
(Our bodies, again intertwine, in sweat.)
En corps à corps, libérant nos doutes et nos peurs.
(In body to body, releasing our doubts and our fears.)
Que j'aime ton cuir.
(How I love your leather.)

Ton corps exprime sa passion des langues étrangères

(Your body expresses its passion for foreign languages)

Et d'étrange façon, je peints les étagères.

(And in a strange way, I paint the shelves.)

Que j'aime ton cuir... Tes yeux, ton sourire.

(How I love your leather... Your eyes, your smile.)

Haïti, le 16 novembre 2019

J'AI TANT D'AMOUR
A DONNER
SO MUCH LOVE TO GIVE

Nos sentiments ont grandi avec le temps
(Our feelings have grown with time)
A profiter, chaque jour, de l'instant présent.
(Enjoying every day, the present moment.)
Tu m'as promis une histoire d'amour, à la vie à la mort,
(You promised me a love story, life and death,)
Pour nous soumettre, à tour de rôle, à la loi du plus fort.
(To submit us, in turn, to the law of the strongest.)

Les coups de canif ont lacéré nos cœurs trop purs
(The blows of knife have lacerated our too pure hearts)
En éclats de voix, de vaisselle brisée, de mots trop durs.
(In bursts of voice, broken dishes, words too hard.)
A force d'imaginer le pire, la guerre s'est imposée.
(By dint of imagining the worst, war has imposed itself.)
Violence, doutes et trahisons nous ont divisés.
(Violence, doubts and betrayals divided us.)

Pourtant...
Yet...

Aujourd'hui, tu le sais, j'ai tant d'amour à donner.
(Today, you know, I have so much love to give.)
Tant d'amour tous les jours,
(So much love every day,)
Tant d'amour pour toujours.
(So much love forever.)
J'ai tant d'amour à donner
(I have so much love to give)
Tant d'amour à donner.
(So much love to give.)

Il y en a eu des joies. Il y en a eu des peines.
(There have been joys. There have been sorrows.)
Des nuits de crises, à piétiner nos haines.
(Nights of crisis, trampling on our hatreds.)
Tant de fautes avouées, à demi pardonnées
(So many faults confessed, half forgiven)
Et tu es parti. Notre histoire d'amour s'est achevée.
(And you left. Our love story ended.)

Nos cœurs blessés emplis de chagrin et de regrets.
(Our wounded hearts filled with sorrow and regret.)
Je reviens vers toi, à genoux, implorant la paix.
(I come back to you, on my knees, begging for peace.)
Laisse-moi redevenir la petite fille que tu aimais.
(Let me become again the little girl you loved.)
Accepte mon amour, pour toi, sans condition.
(Accept my love, for you, unconditionally.)

Car...
Because...

Aujourd'hui, tu le sais, j'ai tant d'amour à donner.
(Today, you know, I have so much love to give.)
Tant d'amour tous les jours,
(So much love every day,)
Tant d'amour pour toujours.
(So much love forever.)
J'ai tant d'amour à donner
(I have so much love to give)
Tant d'amour à donner.
(So much love to give.)

Aujourd'hui, tu le sais, j'ai tant d'amour à donner.
(Today, you know, I have so much love to give.)
Tant d'amour tous les jours,
(So much love every day,)
Tant d'amour pour toujours.
(So much love forever.)
J'ai tant d'amour à donner
(I have so much love to give)
Tant d'amour à donner.
(So much love to give.)

28 décembre 2018

POUR N'AIMER QUE TOI
TO ONLY LOVE YOURSELF

Dès le premier regard, lorsque je vous ai rencontré,
(From the first moment I met you,)
Chéri, j'ai su que notre amour durerait toujours.
(Honey, I knew our love would last forever.)
Vous ne me quittiez pas des yeux. Des sentiments plus forts chaque jour,
(You never took your eyes off me. Stronger feelings, every day,)
On s'est promis une histoire d'amour, à la vie à la mort,
(We promised each other a love story, life and death,)

Chaque jour je pense à vous, mes moments de bonheur.
(Every day I think of you, my moments of happiness.)
C'est mon histoire d'amour ; Je crois aussi que c'est la vôtre.
(That's my love story; I also believe it is yours.)
Chaque soir, je retrouve ma place près de votre cœur.
(Every evening, I find my place close to your heart.)
Vous êtes devenu maître de mes pensées et moi des vôtres.
(You have become master of my thoughts and I of yours.)

Je ferai n'importe quoi pour n'aimer que toi.
(I will do anything to only love you.)
Je serai ta reine, tu seras mon roi.
(I will be your queen, you will be my king.)
Je serai toujours là pour toi

(I'll always be there for you)

Pour n'aimer que toi.

(To only love you.).)

Certaines nuits nous lâchons nos éclats de voix,

(Some nights we let our voices out,)

Vos plus beaux sourires emplissent mon cœur de joies.

(Your most beautiful smiles fill my heart with joy.)

Tous les matins, j'aime vos messages de tendresse de vive voix.

(Every morning I love your messages of tenderness)

Je vous offre mon amour sans condition. C'est mon choix.

(I offer you my love without condition. It is my choice.)

Je ferai n'importe quoi pour n'aimer que toi.

(I will do anything to only love you.).)

Je serai ta reine, tu seras mon roi.

(I will be your queen, you will be my king.)

Je serai toujours là pour toi

(I'll always be there for you)

Pour n'aimer que toi.

(To only love you.).)

Je vous donne mon amour, vous m'apportez du bonheur.

(I give you my love, you bring me happiness.)

Je sais que, chaque jour, notre rencontre nous enchante.

(I know that every day we meet, we are enchanted.)

Lorsque je suis sur scène, c'est pour vous que je chante.

(When I am on stage, it is for you that I sing.)

Mes fans, vous connaissez mes chansons par cœur.

(My fans, you know my songs by heart.)

Je ferai n'importe quoi pour n'aimer que toi.

(I will do anything to only love you.)

Je serai ta reine, tu seras mon roi.

(I will be your queen, you will be my king.)

Je serai toujours là pour toi

(I'll always be there for you)

Pour n'aimer que toi.

(To only love you.).)

LA NUIT, ELLE BOIT SES MOTS AT NIGHT, SHE DRINKS HER WORDS

La nuit, elle boit ses mots pour oublier ses rêves.
(At night, she drinks her words to forget her dreams.)
Pour éviter qu'elle crève, avec ses cigarettes.
(To prevent her from dying with her cigarettes.)

Elle vide ses verres de peine
(She empties her glasses of sorrow)
L'amour ne se donne pas la peine
(Love does not bother)
De la prévenir.
(To warn her.)
Ils n'ont plus d'avenir.
(No longer any future.)

Elle étouffe ses lumières
(She stifles her lights)
Et crache ses colères.
(And spits out her anger.)

La nuit, elle boit ses mots pour oublier ses rêves.
(At night, she drinks her words to forget her dreams.)
Pour éviter qu'elle crève, avec ses cigarettes.
(To prevent her from dying with her cigarettes.)

Tous ses reproches, il ne peut plus les supporter.
(All her reproaches, he can't stand them anymore.)
Elle menace de le tuer.
(She threatens to kill him.)

L'amour se construit sur l'espoir du bonheur
(Love is built on the hope of happiness)
Elle parle seule, jusqu'à pas d'heure.
(She speaks alone, until noon.)

La nuit, elle boit ses mots pour oublier ses rêves.
(At night, she drinks her words to forget her dreams.)
Pour éviter qu'elle crève, avec ses cigarettes.
(To prevent her from dying with her cigarettes.)

Elle aimerait vivre sa passion
(She'ld like to live her passion)
Mais doit écouter sa raison.
(But must listen her reason.)

Elle n'a plus de limite.
(She has no more limits.)
La vie s'écoule trop vite.
(Life goes by too fast.)

La nuit, elle boit ses mots pour oublier ses rêves.
(At night, she drinks her words to forget her dreams.)
Pour éviter qu'elle crève, avec ses cigarettes.
(To prevent her from dying with her cigarettes.)

Ses maux du soir sont bien trop lourds
(Her evening pains are far too heavy)
Dans le souterrain de velours.
(In the velvet underground.)

Artiste immortel, tu tenailles
(Immortal artist, you hold)
Des créations dans ses entrailles.
(Creations in her entrails.)

La nuit, elle boit ses mots pour oublier ses rêves.
(At night, she drinks her words to forget her dreams.)
Pour éviter qu'elle crève, avec ses cigarettes.
(To prevent her from dying with her cigarettes.)

Il t'a fait des promesses impossibles
(You made impossible promises)
Et tout ça te rend irascible.
(And all this makes you irritable.)

Le caramel fait fondre ta carapace
(The caramel melts your shell)
Entre tes pinces de rapace.
(Between your claws of raptor.)

La nuit, elle boit ses mots pour oublier ses rêves.
(At night, she drinks her words to forget her dreams.)
Pour éviter qu'elle crève, avec ses cigarettes.
(To prevent her from dying with her cigarettes.)

NORMA JEAN

Tu peux user tes jeans, (You can wear out your jeans,)
Te faire appeler Norma Jean, (To call you Norma Jean,)
Ou abuser de caféine mais… (Or overindulge in caffeine but..)

Touche pas à la cocaïne, si tu veux être… mon héroïne.
(Don't touch cocaine, if you want to be... my heroin.)

Tu mélanges vodka et gin (You mix vodka and gin)
Comme Pierrot et Colombine (Like Pierrot and Colombine)
J'veux pas jouer à copain - copine, mais…
(I don't want to play boyfriend / girlfriend, but...)

Touche pas à la cocaïne, si tu veux être… mon héroïne.
(Don't touch cocaine, if you want to be... my heroin.)

Sur ton nombril un piercing (On your belly button a piercing)
Et sur mon dos, tu dessines (And on my back, you draw)
Un biker sur sa machine (A biker on his machine).

Tu fais glisser mon jean, (You're slipping my jeans,)
Tu te lèches les babines (You lick your lips)
Quand tu caresses …ma copine, mais…
(When you caress...my girlfriend, but...)

Touche pas à la cocaïne, si tu veux être… mon héroïne.
(Don't touch cocaine, if you want to be... my heroin.)

CHANSON D'AMOUR NOT A LOVE SONG

(Cette chanson d'amour n'est pas pour toi)

(This love song is a not for you)

Mon bébé m'a quitté ; seul je vais habiter Un grand appart bien vide.

(My baby has left me; alone I will live in a big, empty apartment.)

Mon coeur aussi est vide.

(My heart is empty too.)

Dîners en amoureux, ballades et plateaux télé,

(Lovers' dinners, romantic walks and TV sets,)

Mon amour pour toi, aussi, tu l'as tout dépensé.

(My love for you, you spent it all, too.)

Je chante l'amour. Mes musiciens jouent fort.

(I sing about love. My musicians play loudly.)

Pourtant derrière mes sourires que les fans adorent,

(Yet behind my smiles and music that fans love,)

Je suis seul, le cœur et les mains couvertes de chaînes.

(I am alone, my heart and hands covered with chains.)

Je chante l'amour. Je ne connais pas la haine. Mais…

(I sing about love. I don't know about hate. But...)

Cette chanson d'amour n'est pas pour toi.

(This love song is not for you.)

Tu t'es bien trop moquée de moi. Tu vois,

(You've been laughing at me too much. You see,)
Cette chanson d'amour n'est plus pour toi.
(This love song is no longer for you.)

Je regarde les danseuses, sur la scène,
(I look at the dancers on the stage,)
Mais mon regard est absent. Personne ne t'aime.
(But my gaze is absent. No one loves you.)

Mon amour, tu m'as trahi. Mon amour, tu m'as quitté
(My love, you betrayed me. My love, you left me)
Ne me laissant que mes yeux pour pleurer.
(Leaving me only my eyes to cry.)
Je chante l'amour. Je dois sourire.
(I sing about love. I have to smile.)
Quand tout, au fond de moi, me fait souffrir.
(When everything deep down inside makes me suffer.)

Tu m'as quitté, mais je ne suis pas désespéré.
(You left me, but I'm not desperate.)
Et, tu le sais, je n'ai jamais pleuré.
(And, you know, I've never cried.)

Cette chanson d'amour n'est pas pour toi.
(This love song is not for you.)
Tu t'es bien trop moquée de moi. Tu vois,
(You've been laughing at me too much. You see,)
Cette chanson d'amour n'est plus pour toi.
(This love song is no longer for you.)

Tes lèvres me faisaient fermer les yeux, dans le noir,
(Your lips knew to close my eyes in the dark,)
Sur quelle peau vont-elles se poser, ce soir ?
(On what skin will they be landing on tonight?)
Tu disais « pour toujours » et « à jamais »
(You said "forever" and "ever")
Mais un nouvel amour, aujourd'hui, t'a remplacée.
(But a new love today has replaced you).

Cette chanson d'amour n'est pas pour toi.
(This love song is not for you.)
Tu t'es bien trop moquée de moi. Tu vois,
(You've been laughing at me too much. You see,)

Cette chanson d'amour n'est plus pour toi.
 (This love song is no longer for you.)

Cette chanson d'amour n'est pas pour toi.
 (This love song is not for you.)
Tu t'es bien trop moquée de moi. Tu vois,
(You've been laughing at me too much. You see,)
Cette chanson d'amour n'est plus pour toi.
(This love song is no longer for you.)

SI TU N'VEUX PAS DEV'NIR MON EX IF YOU DON'T WANNA BE MY EX

Descend-moi dans le Sussex (Take me down again to Sussex)
Viens caresser mon latex (Come and caress my latex)
Tu n'es pas une fille qu'on vexe (You're not a girl who gets offended)
Même si moi je te rend perplexe (Even if I make you perplexed).

J'ai des idées dans mon cortex (I have ideas in my cortex)
Qui vont te donner des complexes (That's gonna make you nervous).
Arrose tes seins de Contrex (Water your breasts with Contrex)
Caresses bien tes parties annexes (And caress your ancillary areas).

Emmène moi dans les rues d'Aix (Take me to the streets of Aix)
Redresse-toi et mate mon erex... (Straighten up so I can check out your erect...)
Et occupe toi de mon sexe (And take care of my sex)
Si tu n'veux pas dev'nir mon ex (If you don't want to become my ex).

Je suis dur comme du silex (I am as hard as flint
Garde au chaud mon erex...(Keep warm my erex...)
Débrouilles toi pout être ambidextre (Make sure you're ambidextrous)
Sur toi coulera ma circonflex... (On your skin will flow the wax that we flexe)

Emmène-moi dans les rues d'Aix (Take me to the streets of Aix)
Redresse-toi et mate mon erex… (Straighten up so I can check out your erect)
Et occupe toi de mon sexe (And take care of my sex)
Si tu n'veux pas dev'nir mon ex (If you don't want to become my ex).

Si par malheur pour toi tu m' vexes (If, unfortunately, you hurt my feelings for you),
Avec un fouet je dessinerai des cercles, Alex (With a whip, I'll draw circles Alex).
Sur les jolis globes de tes fesses (On the pretty globes of your butt).

J'ai des idées dans mon cortex (I have ideas in my cortex)
Qui vont te donner des complexes (That's gonna make you nervous).
Arrose tes seins de Contrex (Water your breasts with Contrex)
Caresses bien tes parties annexes (And caress your ancillary areas).

Si tu n'veux pas dev'nir mon ex (If you don't want to become my ex).
Si tu n'veux pas dev'nir mon ex (If you don't want to become my ex).

ROCKSTAR FOREVER

Text : Alain Zirah

Music : Bernard Ramel

Quand je serai Rockstar, je serai guitariste
(When I am Rockstar, I will be a guitarist)
Avec des lunettes noires et puis aussi pianiste.
(With dark glasses and also a pianist.)

Je serai décadent, voyou, androgyne.
(I will be decadent, bad boy, androgynous.)
Je t'enlèverai ton string et ton jean.
(I'll take off your thong and your jeans.)

Rockstar forever, Rockstar forever,
Rockstar forever, Rockstar.

Quand je serai Rockstar, je serai le leader
(When I am Rockstar, I will be the leader)
D'un groupe de jeunes filles de toutes les couleurs,
(Of a group of young girls of all colors,)

Toujours merveilleuses, sur scène comme au lit.
(Wonderful as ever, on stage and in bed.)
Elles m'aimeront, deux par deux, sans aucune jalousie.
(They will love me, two by two, without any jealousy.)

Rockstar forever, Rockstar forever,
Rockstar forever, Rockstar.

Quand je serai Rockstar, je serai excentrique,
(When I am Rockstar, I will be eccentric,)
Habillé de foulards, de tuniques synthétiques.
(Dressed in scarves, synthetic tunics.)

Je me prostituerai pour la scène, en violet,
(I will prostitute myself for the stage, in purple,)
Et te déshabillerai sans vouloir te violer.
(And undress you without wanting to rape you.)

Rockstar forever, Rockstar forever,
Rockstar forever, Rockstar.

Rockstar forever, Rockstar forever,
Rockstar forever, Rockstar.

Make up collé sur le miroir de ma loge,
(Make up stuck on the mirror of my dressing room,)
Je renverserai ton lipstick jusqu'au fond de ta gorge.
(I'll spill your lipstick down your throat.)

Toute la nuit, de plaisirs accélérés,
(All night long, of accelerated pleasures,)
D'amour, sans cesse, je te maquillerai.
(With love, unceasingly, I will make you up.)

Rockstar forever, Rockstar forever,
Rockstar forever, Rockstar.

Rockstar forever, Rockstar forever,
Rockstar forever, Rockstar.

ALONE AND LONELY

Seul, si seul, (Alone and lonely,)
Je ne suis plus que l'ombre de ton regard
(I'm just a shadow of your eyes now)
Depuis que tu es partie. (Since you left.)
J'use mes doigts sur des cordes de guitare
(I make my fingers bleed on guitar strings)
Pour me redonner envie. (To make me want it back.)

Seule, si seule, (Alone and lonely,)
Tu promènes ton sac à dos de gare en gare
(You walk your backpack from station to station)
Et t'abandonnes dans des parties
(And you give up in games)
Ivre de vie, tu le sais tu t'égares
(Drunk with life, you know you're going astray)
Mais je n'abandonnerai pas la partie.
(But I won't give up the game.)

Pour toi, je frime, stetson et gros cigare,
(For you, I'm showing off, stetson and big cigar,)
Je m'introduis et me glisses dans tes parties
(I sneak in and slip into your parts)
Les plus intimes…Là, c'est moi qui m'égare.
(The most intimate… Now I'm the one who's getting lost.)
Reviens-moi, redonne mois l'appétit.
(Come back to me, give me back my appetite.)

Les yeux embués, nos retrouvailles dans une gare
(Our eyes fogged up, our reunion in a station)
Font péter les étoiles. On va gagner la partie
(Make the stars fart. We're going to win the game.)

Ensemble. Dans les lieux insolites, sans égards,
(Together. In unusual places, regardless,)
On va se remettre à faire des p'tits.
(We're gonna start making little babies.)

Seuls, plus seuls, (Alone, lonely no more,)
Nous ne serons plus seul à seule.
(We'll no longer be alone.)
Seul à seule, Nous ne serons plus seul à seule.
(Alone, alone, we'll no longer be alone.)

A MALE FOR YOU

I don't want to hurt you,
I don't want to see you cry.
I don't want to waste your time,
I just want to make you fall in love.

I don't want to depress you.
I don't want to make you feel wrong.
I don't want to tell you about it.
Just make you crazy about me.

Love me to forget you.
Love me to tear yourself apart.
Love me to the last breath to
Just make you crazy about me.

I just want to make you smile.
I just want to see you grow up.
I just want to make you happy.
Just make you fall in love.

I like to see you turn your back.
And make me forget your whims.
I'm sneaking up on your back
To caress your smooth skin.

Love me to forget you.
Love me to tear yourself apart.
Love me to the last breath.
Just make you crazy about me.

I like the sun on your black skin.
Your butt waving in the bathtub.
The secrets of your old grimoire
Captured in the dark night.

I like to see you turn your back.
And make me forget your whims.
I'm sneaking up on your back
To caress your smooth skin.

Love me to forget you.
Love me to tear myself apart.
Love me to the last breath.
Just make you crazy about me.

VERANE

Verane, for you life is not a drama.
You live it with your soul
Of children with big eyes
glowing.

Verane, with your smile and charm
Which, quite often, disarms me,
You're hiding in your bamboo cabin.
You lie down and get high,
Slowly.

Verane, don't burn your soul.
With them. Let me varnish your soul.
They make you suffer and are not worth it
Let me make you a queen,
Slowly.

Verane, your smile of pearls and diamonds
Knows how to fan the flames. That's charming.
Also, pass your varnish on my soul
While you're on the phone, you're on fire.
For hours, you're out of control.
Tenderly.

Verane, don't burn your soul
Of children with big eyes
glowing.

SWEET DEMON

Sweetie Demon, scatter your splendor.
Angel of perversity, let your beauty flow forth.
A heretical jewel with long cosmic loops
Without mercy, offer me your cruel love.

Softy Demon with slow caresses,
Fill me with your purity; Lose your virginity.
In the ocean arms of a synthetic sun
Spit out your flames and invade my soul.

Sweetie Demon, wipe your tears.
Get out of your video coffin, little squirrel.
Suck my blood with your satanic kisses.
Offer to my damned soul your pleasures of immortality.

Softy Demon, scatter your splendor in nothingness.
Dry your tears like a little girl in bloom, forget the giants.
Lose your virginity in the icy flames of my ocean love.
Come and satisfy your lover, adulterate the eye of your silver mirror.

Decadent cloud, decaying wind,
Shade of mystery hovering over the Earth,
You glide in ecstasy, you come on the ground
And I'm desperate in the void.

NEVER ALONE
AGAIN, BABY

Tonight, by the fireplace,
I'm listening to your heartbeat. I found you.
You'll never be alone again, baby.

A single word from the tip of your lips
And I will always be there for you.
Only for you, I'll be there.

Your closed eyes ignore my feelings
When your mouth calls for love,
When your mouth is love,

I'm listening to your heartbeat. I found you.
You'll never be alone again, baby.

Perched on golden heels,
You only inspire love, my beloved baby.
The sun dances on your tanned legs,
And your complicit look keeps getting me drunk.

I'm listening to your heartbeat. I found you.
You'll never be alone again, baby.

I'm listening to your heartbeat. I found you.
You'll never be alone again, baby.

WHO ARE YOU BREATHING FOR?

The rain is running down the window and I'm thinking of you,
You're far from me and I can't see it.
You're far from me and you don't know it.

Who else could warm my heart
When only you can heal my wounds?

I think of you dancing and laughing,
While in the cold of love, I write to you.

For you, I would like to grow up, to become
The man you admire,
The man you admire,
The man you're breathing for.

Eyes glued to the window of grief,
In my memories, I'm looking for you
Your image is sometimes so distant.

You will stay forever in my heart
Even if you are, forever, away from me,
In silence, in pain, I'm thinking about you.

For you, I wanted to grow up, to become
The man you admire,
The man you admire,
The man you breathe.

But you left me with the man you admire,
The man you admire,
The man you're breathing for.

And one day, the man left you
For the woman that he admires
For the one he breathes.
The one he breathes...

IMPERFECT CRIME

You told me you loved me.
The meal should have been perfect,
Carbonizing your package, hanging on the phone
With all your girlfriends, you left me on the phone.

The rest was almost perfect.
And the meal for both of us was imperfect.
In silence, when sleep has won over you.
All night long, beside your sleeping body, I cried.

Your scream should have been perfect.
But love, in silence, struck you.
With your blood, the cushion was soaked.

No remorse, no dignity!
Behind jailhouse bars, kneeling,
I'm crying. You are missing my life, forever.

The film was almost perfect.
You laughed a lot when you watched it.
The scream was almost imperfect.
Your smiles have condemned me to love you.
Forever.

WE'RE NOT GOING TO MOVE ON

Remember that wonderful day
When we first met, we were not old.

Our eyes crossed,
And our hands never left each other.

Remember that first day
Where you gave me your love.
All night and all day long,
Behind the closed shutters, we made love.

I remember, it was a Saturday,
It could have been a Friday.
Many of them danced around us,
But, on the dancefloor of my heart,
There was only you and me.

Your body and my heart, so tightly packed,
Beat the rhythm, soaked, in unison.
Hairless, your sweat pussy, animated by the rage,
Danced on my velvet dreams the riffs of your wild music.

Remember that first day
Where you gave me your love.
Our eyes crossed,
And our hands never left each other.

At twenty, you have all the audacity
So today, believe me, please,
We're not going to move on.

BULLET TRAIN BLUES

Text : Alain Zirah

Translate : Herve Lechevalier

Paris-Marseille, Marseille-Paris,
Like a silly old thing, alone on my crumpled bed.
I count the hours. I cry and I write
The dancing words, my dreams
And I have the blues, the Paris blues.

Marseille-Paris, Paris-Marseille,
From town to town, like a bee,
I frolic and flirt in the bullet train, putting many miles
In order to get lucky. I'm beyond myself.
Like a mad dog, I burn my money,
And I have the blues, the Marseille blues.

Avignon, Toulon, Aix-en-Provence,
Looking for my girlfriends… my ex,
I'll go from city to city, that's for sure,
Because I have the blues, the Bullet Train blues.

I wake up on Paradis street (Marseille), Cours Mirabeau
(Aix-en-Provence),
I am lunching on the Champs Elysee (Paris) at noon
and go to a disco party Between clubs :
Trolleybus, Bains Douche, Mistral and Palace
And I have the blues, the nine to five job blues.

Avignon, Toulon, Aix-en-Provence,
In the pictures of my girlfriends… my ex,
I'll go from city to city, that's for sure, I'll get out of here.
Because I have the blues, the Bullet Train blues.

On a beach, with you, I'll go,
And only you will I admire,
You'll know how to bewitch me
And to always make me forget
The blues, the Bullet Train blues.

MY PAPER ALLIGATOR

Text : Alain Zirah

Translate : Herve Lechevalier

Orange hair, forehead and silver lips,
You play with the words, you fascinate the teenagers.
Under your foreigner's top hat from somewhere else,
Your shyness challenges your ego.

Body wrapped in colors, you remain motionless
When we come to tear off your white kimono.
Timeless figure, fetish object to worship,
You're playing the multifaceted chameleon,
That's so silly.

You write the words, dance with the fireplaces
And the iguana flirts in the velvet underground.
With you, my paper alligator.

White oxygenated bronze silhouette,
You shine the neon lights from Tokyo to Sidney.

Elegant alligator in its frock jacket,
You're thinking to me, when the fish are dancing,
With their tattooed navel and pierced ears,
You, my paper alligator.

Show us the way to the City of Angels.
Oh, yeah, I forgot, you're afraid of Americans,
And the iguana flirts in the velvet underground.
With you, my paper alligator.

BETTINA

Bettina if you leave me now,
Going far away from me,
You know that, you're getting lost
If you take me away from you.

Bettina, don't go away,
The grass is not greener over there.
Everyone will tell you that,
I'm only thinking about you.

Bettina, when you leave,
So far away from me.
You know you're getting lost,
You only think about me.

Bettina, don't go away,
Your life won't be any better there.
Everyone will tell you that,
I love you and only you.

Bettina, if you forget me,
What would my life become then.
Everyone will tell you that,
I only love you.

My exceptional muse
So beautiful, so beautiful
You always smile close to me
And I only sing for you.

Bettina, you'll be back,
The sun was not shining any better there.
And soon, you'll tell me,
That you only love me.

Bettina, you will stay,
The sun will shine here for you.
And every day, we'll say it again
That you love me and only me,
And I love you and only you.

LIVE YOUR LIFE

Text : Alain Zirah

Translate : Herve Lechevalier

You're looking at the red convertibles in front of the big hotel,
And you hesitate. You wait for your chance.

At the airport, you can imagine the far away countries
In such prestigious destinations.
And you watch the trains pass by. In vain.

Yet,
Take your chance when it comes,
Catch the flight, take the first train
And you'll have a great life.
Live your life in a Ferrari. Live your life, baby.

No more waking up in a briefcase
Soon you'll face the crowd of your fans
Goodbye nine to five.

Live your life in a Ferrari. Live your life, baby.

All it takes is one song that rhymes
With a little, a lot of showmanship.
Take your chance when it comes,
Catch the flight, the first train
And you'll have a great life.

Live your life in a Ferrari. Live your life, baby.

Porsche ride in the palaces,
Collects gadgets and thousand-dollar bills
No need for a talisman or a charm,
Play video clip, but never freak out.

Live your life in a Ferrari. Live your life, baby.

Seek the great love of your childhood dreams
Don't take yourself seriously,
Take your chance when it comes,
Catch the flight, the first train
And you'll have a great life.

Live your life in a Ferrari. Live your life, baby.

Video clip your life on an old guitar,
Paint electric colors in the late evening,
But always, remain you, natural and persevering,
Likes emotions but lives in the present time.
Be true to yourself.

Take your chance when it comes,
Catch the flight, take the first train
And you'll have a great life.
Live your life in a Ferrari. Live your life, baby.

And you'll get your red corvette.
You'll get it if you move.
Redheads, blond or brunette fixed
On film and glossy paper.
Open your eyes. Only one of them is for you.

She's waiting for you on the dock.
Come on, move it. Move it.

Take your chance when it comes,
Catch the flight, take the first train
And you'll have a great life.

Live your life in a Ferrari. Live your life, baby.

SYMPATHY FOR THE WACKO

Text : Alain Zirah

Translate : Herve Lechevalier

Be careful, I'm crazy.
I no longer reasonable,
Be careful, I am you
And my name is everywhere.

My name is Lucifer,
I think you'll like it.
You'll have to get used to it.

Pack your things,
I'm taking you to hell.

Be careful, I'm Them,
A vaporous demon
Who sees everything through your eyes
And they all die.

My name is Lucifer,
I think you'll like it.
"You'll have to get used to it.

Pack your things,
I'm taking you to hell.

IN MY STREET

The people who pass through my street,
Why do they have to kill each other?

Why do people go to war?
To people they've never seen before?
Precisely because they've never seen them before.

All you'll have to do is love them,
Listen to them, respect them.

The people who pass through my street,
Why do they go to war?
To people they've never seen before?

All you'll have to do is love them,
Listen to them, respect them.

The malformed and the bumpy,
All the mutants that pass through my street.

DANCE YOUR LIFE

Listen to this music going down to your toes,
Look around you, we're not mystics.
I want to catch your eyes, listen to this music.
If you don't look at me, I'll send you mosquitoes

Tonight, on the dance floor, I see only you.
I want to make you happy, to take you under my roof.
I'm going to make you happy because I only see you.
Dance your life, tonight our bodies will marvel.

Under the sunlight's, in the rain or on the back seat,
Under a porch, on hot sand or in winter snow
In the elevator that will put us in trouble
Baby, believe me, tonight you'll smile at me.

I'm going to make you happy because I only see you.
Dance your life, tonight our bodies will marvel.
Dance your life, tonight our bodies will marvel.

Listen to this music going down to your toes,
Look around you, we're not mystics.
I want to catch your eyes, listen to this music.
If you don't look at me, I'll send you mosquitoes

I'm going to make you happy because I only see you.
Dance your life, tonight our bodies will marvel.
Dance your life, tonight our bodies will marvel.

SLEEPING ALL NIGHT LONG

The last couples, in the deserted streets,
When you come out of the nightclubs, sweaty,
Suffocating with smoke,
Outside the air is freezing cold. And I'm lonely.

The streets fall asleep, in silence,
Car headlights light up, it's easy,
Looking for easy prey.

Girls are not aware of that!
Rather than going out,
They prefer to sleep... All night long.
Sleep tonight, sleep... All night long.
They prefer to sleep... All night long.

Guys were looking at girls dancing slows in the dark,
Ready to go to bed with an inflatable doll
Because they haven't found the love of their lives.
They came to their parents' house early to sleep.

Girls are not aware of that!
Rather than going out,
They prefer to sleep... All night long.
Sleep tonight, sleep... All night long.
They prefer to sleep... All night long.

Eyes swollen with sleep and blind by the sun;
The guys' fridge is stocked and then they go to bed.
The sheets wrinkled with lonely boredom.

How would girls understand boredom?
Rather than go out,
They prefer to sleep... All night long.
Sleep tonight, sleep... All the night.
They prefer to sleep... All the night.

They prefer to sleep alone and well,
Even getting married with the guy next door
Rather than going out at night.

Girls are not aware of that!
Rather than going out,
They prefer to sleep... All night long.
Sleep tonight, sleep... All night long.
They prefer to sleep... All night long.

IT'S NOT FOR YOU

Text : Alain Zirah

Translate : Herve Lechevalier

They were beautiful and appetizing,
Three of them, lying on fine white sand.
The drops were dripping on their bottoms and on their breasts
And they are tossing around, relentlessly.

There were three of them, young and beautiful and appetizing,.
Speaking of nonsense, giggling, squirming
And the more I looked at them, the more I fell for them.
We should have made a choice; no choice is the right temptation!

Get real ! These girls are not for you.
Get real ! You can't pick up all three.

When the sand sticks to their thighs
And their beautiful breasts looked like ripe fruit
Gorged with sunshine, they stood up, leaned against a wall.
When they went to the sea, all men eyes taped to their thighs.

The everyday mermaids have beautiful tanned legs
And sunglasses look alike Cartier. One balloon is enough
To highlight their chests, bottoms and tanned backs.
Their thongs are as many splashes of color. And worse!

Get real ! these girls are not for you.
Get real ! you can't pick up all three.

When they got back on their bath sheets,
Dripping droplets on the caramel of their skin,
Covered with white sand on their feet and hands,
They looked like Greek statues, made of marble and skin.

A boy came up to me, flamboyant glasses on his nose.
He offered to get to know them and sat down
Next to them. Staring at them like a lost man.
They laughed at him,
Mocked each other nicely. He got up and left, stale.

So I told him:

Get real man! these girls are not for you.
Get real man! you can't pick up all three.

TOO MUCH IN TOO SOON

I have so many things to say
So many books to read
So many texts to sing,
Just give me time to express myself.

I have so much to do.
Texts to be written, drawings to be made
So many things to tell,
Just give me time to express myself.

I got too much in too soon, in too soon
I got too much in too soon, in too soon.

I got my own albums to do
So many films, I imagined I'll do
Lord, let me live so long enough...

I got too much in too soon, in too soon
I got too much in too soon, in too soon.

I got too much in too soon, in too soon
I got too much in too soon, in too soon.

VARNISH ON MY SOUL

Text : Alain Zirah

Translate : Herve Lechevalier

I put varnish on my soul
Some gloss on my lips and on my toes,
You came and go with my grinning soul.
My body's wicked, if you go...

You terrifie my love, step on my lonelyness.
I whip your pride, my lovely priestess.
With arrogance, I tear your wrong feelings
I want you come back to me.

Black in white. Sweet and savage African beauty.
Skin oiled with perfume and coconut milk.
Black skin in white cotton from duty
Free. How could I forget, hand in hand, the silk
Of your lips on my body.

And darkness of your blood.
'cause, angel, so dark is your blood.

You can change the colours of your hair.
Put amethyst on your eyes, black around your lips.
When the music flows, you move your hips.

Don't change your older habits.
You can't run away for love.
The man will remain hidden in your shadow.

We've been so far away
But love forever still beating, someday,
In sharp trousers moving on the dancefloor.

Don't change your older habits
Honey, you can't run away your love
The man will remain hidden in your shadow.
I store your body images inside my camera lens
To tattoo your smile under my eyelids.

Don't be afraid by Love.
In spite of my white skin, Ebony and ivory live together in perfect
harmony.
I'll light up your life.
Honey, you can't run away your love
Just stay forever in my life.

And I'll still be the man that you always love
With ivory of my skin, I'll light up your life.
And I'll stay the man hidden in your shadow.

Marseilles –The Paradox – 03/09/2007

ARISTOCRATIC PUNK

THE BIG CHESS GAME

PUNK is a rigged chess game
Lost in three sets:

- THE REVOLUTION against suffering, injustice and the power of money.

- HATH towards anything that doesn't have green hair or epic pork hairstyle.

- THE DESPIRATION to realize that the game is rigged from the beginning and that fighting is worth nothing more than weakening....

And we decide to become assisted!

"-Alain Zirah, you are the spiritual son of Nietzsche!"

(Ferdinand Lallemand, philosophy teacher
at Perier high school – 1976)

I read Nietzsche's books and discover a man which advocated the cult of the homo superior and the nihilism. And I realized that Superman, Batman, Spider- Man and Conan the barbarian were the supermen whose comics I was reading.
Bowie, the Stones, the supermen I admired.

Lou Reed, Iggy Pop and the punks conveyed the image of nihilism and the fake reality, as Alice Cooper who sang he wanted to be elected as President of United States. Nobody could imagine, forty years later, it became possible for a TV reality actor. (Alain Zirah – Marseilles – September 2019)

NO FUTURE:
PUNK 1977-2007-?

On his T-shirt was written "NO FUTURE"
And "LOBOTOMY" on his jacket.

He was hanging out in the streets with a show.
His naked skull covered with a golden film.
In his eyes, no hope was shining,
But he kept on living.... out of habit.

Last classy guy in a dirty world
Overcrowded with normal people, megalo-mytho
He came and went in the streets of the city,
Turned back and started again.

Looking for a coin? Certainly, not!
He was looking for a girl to love,
But there were so many people...
Too many girls in the world!

And the streets continued to pour their fashion:
Plastic panther women, peroxide blondes
Trendy pants showing their calves, tennis girls with a scarf on their heads,
Hookers and middle-class women in the same khaki shorts and golden jacket,
Indian boots with fringes or second skin of colored leather.

How to choose? Where can I find the rare bird?

There were so many people, all identical, stereotyped.

Too many guys in the world!

Too many girls in the world!

Fashion is so easy to copy

NO FUTURE

Punk in his soul but looking like a London city guy
The fragile teenager refuses to fight...
And he lets himself dive, as prisoner of the city.

He knows he's destroying himself, that there's no way out...
But he doesn't care; he's no longer worth anything.
He has lost all hope.

How can anyone, at 23, be desperate
To the point of prolonging a mental suicide
Which has been going on forever?

Why do we have to hide the fact that we're different
And that we don't want to get into the anthill?
Will we still have to cheat? Lying?

We want to work, though. But where?
We no longer know where to go; we let ourselves go.
We are afraid of loneliness, because we have known it
And that it hurts!

So we hang on, like a raft,
To a little hope, to someone, to save his life...
And we survive.

SHOCK ME!

Alone, before midnight,
In my cement cage,
As an animal, I suffer from claustrophobia.

On full moon nights,
The beast inside me takes over.
I have to get out, at all costs.

Werewolf, in the deserted city, I wander around
Looking for a girl....

Not to suck her blood,
Just to savour her honey and kiss her breast.

No matter where you are
As long as there's not enough light.
At the corner of a street, an empty beach, or elsewhere
Anywhere!

Suddenly, bursting the dark and silent darkness,
The rattling of stiletto heels cheerfully tinged
Near a nightclub.

A girl walks around with a shuffle.
She's tipsy and not really a queen of beauty,
But she walks alone in the night, so it doesn't matter!

In the smell of fresh blood, tears
mixed with sweat and urine,

The midnight walker struck again.
And finally make love with her under a porch in a deserted street.

I CAN'T GET NO SATISFACTION

You spend your time
Wasting your time.

You would like to live,
But you have to survive.

You want to be free
But you remain a prisoner
Behind your desk.

You want to be you,
Create your universe....
But you have to endure
And you suffer.

If you would take time,
Then you could be a genius,
But you're stuck.
In your nine to five life.

With courage, you could shout
To tell yourself : -" I exist! »
But what's the point?

You don't even have...
Time to live.

THE BIG BUG

When the cockroach stresses me out,
And may the sky wet me,
When the night gets long
And the monotonous boredom.

Music is nothing more than noise
And the tears of the water drops.
Love seems far away to me
Even if the girls dance near me....

Not available…

Men all look alike,
Smiling out of duty, out of necessity,
And my life continues to have no purpose.

So, slowly, I slip into sleep.

THE HUGE BUG

The memories have escaped from the archipelago of my memory,
Seeking to attack me, deep inside myself.
The evening images wake up on their own
And they come to lock me up in their cathode cage.

You're calling me paranoid to put a label on me,
To better lock myself in the spider's web of your thoughts.
You call me schizo because I live in my head...
Huge dreams that make the uncreative sick.

My sun was stolen, my nights filled with terror
And Time continues to erase my memories.
Fortunately, the diamond penetrates into the brand new wax
And the music springs forth, fresh and timeless.

Stop that music! Stop that music! Complete the hearing overdose!
Let me mess with these machines that think for me!
Let me face the psychotic crack alone
While the dragons of sadness tear my past apart.

Memories of yesterday and tomorrow, come out in a cascade,
Get away from underneath the rubble of the illusion,
Only then can we talk about the future!

Azed on 10/05/1982

GENERATION 80'S

Insecurity reigns in the cities.
The passers-by, amnesiacs of smiles,
Move their gloomy and anxious masks,
Looking left and right, worried looks.

Old women run across the streets, or almost so,
For fear of being crushed under aggressive cars.
They sometimes stumble, but metal cars
Barely slow down, without stopping.
Think, they might arrive late!

In the evening, the young people patrol from bar to bar,
Hoping to meet the rare bird to love.
But girls are very rare. They don't go out at night anymore.
However, the deserted streets are lit. There's nothing to be afraid of!

And if, by any chance, you get caught in a fight,
Don't count on anyone! Only on your escape!
Your friends will abandon you, cold and indifferent,
Looking for a safe house from where they can see everything
Without risking a lost punch.

Of course, we can always avoid trouble
And then follow each other, at home, on television,
But one day you wake up old: you've lived.

URBAN CHILD

Born in the heart of concrete and vinyl,
I am Azed, the child of the cities.
Always on the streets looking for somewhere else.

Department store windows
And their models make me hard,
Showing off their privacy to better solicit us.

I penetrate, change my skin, take the pose
In front of over-lit mirrors, in fitting rooms,
Even though I know I won't buy anything.

I'm playing characters from a costume ball. Just for fun.
Like a transvestite Alice,
I try golden tunic and even lizard black plastic.

I look like a God with my patent leather boots
And an adventurer in khaki safari jacket.
A hat, a scarf and I'm someone else.

Unfortunately, the mirror breaks in satin sheets.
I come out and, in a flash, I become Alain again.
Good chic, good kind, flirting with reality,

But always in a good mood.
Satisfied!

I go back to the heat of the asphyxiated street
Resuming my quest for the absolute, for abstruse delusions,
In the midst of thousands of strangers at agreed speeds.

As a polite guy, unfortunately too well behaved,
I hold the door to let them through.
When we meet, we say to ourselves: - "Sorry! »
Like giant ants with atrophied antennae.

I feel like a label.
Yet I don't want to be like them.
I don't want to be good. Too good, too much c...

I'm an excessive person, not a conventional boy,
A fragile child, of course, sometimes weird or uncomfortable....
But I want to be me and stay me... here as elsewhere.
But is there anything else out there?

A STRANGE FEELING

Have you ever had the feeling of being a bubble?
Not a balloon or soap bubble;
Just a bubble.

Have you ever felt your body evaporate
And become a floating globe, enlarged at the top,
Immersed in a semi lethargy?

You can no longer think properly.
You are aware that you are living,
But in a timeless universe.

The walls around them seem quite illusory... derisory.
You go down the steps of the spiral staircase
But stay, at all the times, as if suspended,
Head full of clouds.

You feel like you're dead,
And, at the same time, for the first time,
You fully know that you are living....
And it's only temporary!

With every step you take,
The bubble jumps in your head, Like a water level.
It cannot escape or break.

Simply it floats in an empty and soft skull
And we lose consciousness of everything else. We're a bubble!
At least that's the impression I felt
Just before I write these few lines.

I was a bubble.

SPLEEN IN MARS EYE

When everything seems grey to me, while I get up,
I sink for a moment into melancholy,
But I take refuge in the world of my dreams.

I find myself transported to my own Paradise.
Life flows through it, timeless,
Young girls are beautiful
Concrete disappears into the heart of cities,

The bright greenery invades the grayness
And I realize the need
An eternal kingdom, without any retaliation.

Punish, Why? Lying, why? Kill, why?
No one can escape his past actions
When every being, every sensible thing
Can destroy the quiver with a gesture or a word
From which the aggressive arrows will not be able to escape

Neither to reach a being, nor for a mineral
Nor for a plant, a monster, an animal
Because nothing here is done to kill or strike.

When everything is gray in an uncertain world
The asphyxiated city under a thick shroud
Invades Nature that has disappeared in the distance.

When oppression gets me stuck in burned sand
I feel depressed, lonely, misunderstood
In a wild and so-called civilized world.

But I take refuge in the world of my dreams,
Where I'm the hero in a world of real friends.
Where I am finally going, life is eternal
And it flows endlessly, this timeless life.

In this joyful refuge, young people do not need shelter,
The boys are friendly and the girls are beautiful.
Concrete has disappeared in the heart of cities

The bright greenery has invaded the grayness.

And everyone is happy in this Paradise on Earth
And everyone is loved in the eternal Kingdom.

Come with me, beyond the mirror
Beyond the ice is an unknown world
That you can explore, with me, if you want.
I'll show you the most lost corners
Where we can go, in secret, to love each other.

MALAYSIS IN OFFICE

You spend your time wasting your time.
You would like to live,
But you have to survive.

You want to be free,
But you're a prisoner,
Behind your desk.

You want to be you,
Create your universe....
But you have to endure,
And you suffer.

If you had the time,
You'd like to be a genius,
But you're necrosis.
In a job-disco-sleep.

With courage, you could,
To tell you;
To shout: -" I exist! »

But what's the point?
 You don't even......
Time to live.

S.O.S. MADNESS
THE MEMORIES OF
A MADMAN

My name is nobody.
I don't live anywhere.
I think so, but I'm not,
And yet, I exist.

The men gave me a name,
A number and an address.
Who am I? Who am I? Where am I going?
And for what purpose?

I was told that I was a "human"
That I was born on earth
And that I had to work.
Yet sometimes I wonder

If I follow what they say
Or the one I want to be.
I'm not like the others.
Because I want to be immortal.

That's why I'm writing;
So as not to die.

Some people once said
That I was the living, eternal god,
The breath of life, the all-powerful one,
That I was the thought, the radiant energy.

They said I was the supreme power,
The master of the universe and the infinite heavens
The very high king of kings, the impersonal,
The creative spirit... that I was crazy!

But I no longer believe them; I know they lied.
I know that tomorrow I will be swallowed up
In the chaos of time and medicine.

But they won't be able to do anything anymore.
I already feel my mind formless and tormented
That evaporates into evanescent mists
What silently dissects my sinister enemy: DEATH.

ODE TO YOU

You shining in my night,
Who listens to my dreams and lives them,
I just want you to know that, wherever you are,
I write for you; I think of you.

Sun of my life, you delight my heart
And warm my soul. Even at night!
Your dance is that of an elf
And your smile, like a fairy, makes you look like you.

Your appearance is plastic, perfect, blond and golden,
Adored world, but in your soul dances the moon.
For a sleep against your skin, to coil my body
Warm and warm, I give my world of thoughts.

I think of you and bathe in the light
In the hollow of your arms. You smile, full of life,
You lean your head back and laugh.
I look into the hollow of your shoulder and live again.

You, sun that shines, that warms my nights,
In the ocean bubble, in your technology aquarium,
You dance, you play with your feelings and emotions
In front of your DVD. I think of you and I write to you.

YOU OR YOU

You whom I think of so often,
Without ever meeting you,
Do you know how much I miss you sometimes?

How many times have I loved you,
Under different names?

Without being really sure
May it be you!

Life without you is empty
To wait for the phone.
Your eyes are often
The looks I see in my eyes.

Some silhouettes look like you; I
'm chasing them....
But one gesture....and the charm is broken.

Because you're the only one, the only one,
The one I haven't met yet
But when I find you,
I won't let you go back.

AMNESIC MEMORY

My name is nobody,
I come from nowhere.
Who am I? Who am I? Where am I going?
What is the sense of my life?

What will my destiny be?
Does my life have a past?
What is the point of living
If we have to die next?

Am I from somewhere else? Probably!
I am my own God
Or I'm nothing,
An atom without a soul, lost in nothingness.

SMALL LITTLE FISH

I FEEL LIKE AN AGILE FISH.
WHO WOULD BE ASKED TO STEAL.

WITH A LOT OF GOODWILL,
AND ESPECIALLY TWO GOOD FINS -
THE FISH CAN JUMP...

BUT ASK HIM TO SWIM...

REVERIE

On the other side of the mirror
The black shapes no longer exist.
The green bubbles, the red drops,
The blue sky... Everything is color.

The poor humans have disappeared
When the mutants appeared.

In a stormy storm
The sky blushes and the sea turns green.
Lightning flashes yellow green trees
Under the big purple eye, honey color,
A sun drowned in vermeil clouds.

The colourful universe disappears
In a whirlwind of colors.

Suddenly in the reddened night
A silhouette emerges, brandishing its spectrum;
So the mutants go back to sleep
And the poor humans wake up...

DREAM OF AUGUST

On August 24, 2002, the day before I left for London,
I dreamt that the world was governed
By a communist dictatorship.

No door could stay closed.
Anyone could enter at any time
At his neighbor's house. What a mess!

There were some very aggressive young people
And others rather soft and passive.

Permanently, intruders came to your home
And were then expelled by newcomers.
While you yourself are dislodging another family
To get a nice place back that you're looking at.

Everyone spent their time moving!
Anarchy in U.K.! What a mess! Talk about a nightmare!

UNCOMFORTABLE
(ALAD INSANE)

It is not anywhere, everywhere foreign.
He is always alone, looking for someone to call...
Sometimes he wants to have friends,
To dial a random number on the dial And to improvise....

But people wouldn't understand,
Or they wouldn't have time to listen to it.

At other times, he would like to become someone famous,
An actor, a singer, an athlete, a star...
Or just be rich and famous.
But it's so difficult! We have to change cities.

He spends his days writing and drawing,
But nowadays, no one can read anymore.
And his drawings end up in drawers.

He wants to express himself... But no one listens to him.
He screams. He's screaming. He's threatening to break everything.
If only he could change everything....

He likes ultra violence. Not to do harm
But to shock, to be noticed.
He's going to see *A Clockwork Orange and Escape from New York.*

And he dreams that he is hard, strong and handsome.

But when the lights come on again

The dream fades away. And we have to start all over again....

TOO FRAGILE

Evenings that never end with loneliness.
Too eager to waste my time elsewhere.
Too tired to write my memoirs tonight.
I'm thinking tomorrow, maybe. Or next weekend.
But nothing comes out; the leaf remains silent.

The posters keep spitting out
Their vinyl vermeil music.
And the briefcases show their politeness.
I don't know the words they say.

I don't want to be like them!
I don't want to end up like them!

I am told to fight, that life is a struggle.
But I don't want to fight; I don't know.
And I don't have any weapons anyway.

The female inside me also wants to sing,
But she keeps her teenage makeup.

PERVERSE LOOK

Bloodthirsty vampire
With red canines,
Blood-sucking chowder,

Living necrophage,
Ghostly stryge,
I'm destroying your body.

Demon or wisp,
Larva in your femininity,
A she cat with sphinx eyes,

Bitch with golden horns,
Mummy with a slimy body,
With bloody guts,
Let me eat you up!

I seek Death
That animates your body.

NARCISSUS

Who is the man who ever
Hoped to go through the mirror?
Who is the one who, at least for a day,
Wouldn't want to be mistaken for God?

I, the androgynous Apollo, would like to be able to say:
"This polished surface, it's like looking at me,
I went through it and bathed in it. »

The sea is a mirror whose glass is broken.
We can explore the dark depths of it,
But the mirage is brief and the vision is blurry
We must immediately return to the surface....

Otherwise we find ourselves in another universe
Where the body no longer has any reason to exist.
Because only a spirit can evolve there.

SUPERMAN'S SUPER FANTASMS

"In 1938, Jerry Siegel (writing) and Joe Shuster (drawing) created the character of SUPERMAN, the most famous of all superheroes. Today, at an age when some people only think about retirement, SUPERMAN takes stock of his life.

He has saved millions of lives, on Earth and in the universe, and prevented space super-villains and mad scientists from blowing up the planet.

He loved some beautiful women... of platonic love. Alas, his sexual life is a failure... The dead calm.

Only today, to make up for lost time and for the first time, he uses the only power he has always neglected: the super-fantasy.
This collection of texts and collages by Alain "AZ" Zirah is a brilliant testimony of this. Armed with scissors, cutters, glue and patience, he does not hesitate to tear apart piles of magazines and adjust words for a crazy result, beyond neo-surrealism."

Préface

C'est en 1938 que Jerry Siegel (textes) et Joe Shuster (dessins) font naître le personnage de SUPERMAN, le plus célèbre des super-héros. Aujourd'hui, à l'age où certains ne pensent qu'à leur retraite, SUPERMAN fait le bilan de sa vie.

Il a sauvé des millions de vies, sur la Terre et dans l'univers, empêché quantité de super-voyous de l'espace et de scientifiques un peu allumés de faire sauter leur planète.

Il a aimé quelques jolies femmes… d'amours platoniques. Hélas, sa vie sexuelle est un échec… Le calme plat.

Aujourd'hui seulement, pour rattraper le temps perdu et pour la première fois, il utilise le seul super-pouvoir qu'il a toujours négligé : le super-fantasme.

Ce recueil de textes et de collages réalisés par AZED en est le brillant témoignage. Armé de ciseaux, de cutters, de colle et de patience, il n'hésite pas à mettre en pièce des piles de magazines pour un résultat déjanté au delà du surréalisme.

FOREWORD

I would like to thank, mostly, all those, unknown or known, photographers, actresses, actors, extras, directors, imaginary directors, politicians, creative and advertising men and women, etc... who, voluntarily or involuntarily, participated in the realization of the SUPERMAN'S SUPERFANTASMS.

Through their presence, voluntary or involuntary, they contribute to our great struggle against this deadly disease, this scourge of the century called AIDS, which in English is called AIDS, as if to ask for help.

May one day (as close as possible, please...) a doctor discover the vaccine that will save many human lives. And which, by the way, will finally prevent us from having to wear condoms in these most beautiful moments of love.

Thank you to you, creators of fantasies and imagination. Thanks to you for all your beautiful pictures.
Thank you for igniting our senses and our imagination. Thanks to the provocative fantasies on glossy paper.

And thanks to the women who make men dream by using their pretty legs to do more than just walk.

Alain ZIRAH

THE INFLUENCES OF AZ

1973. Alain ZIRAH discovers science fiction through a novel by LANGELAAN, MEMORIES OF THE ANTI-WORLD; the mark will remain indelible and will change the innocent reader which became AZ.

Among the news, *The Fly*, which will be taken up in 1987 by David CRONENBERG for the cinema. NINA HAGEN, the muse of rock, the electric diva, for her outrageous madness and spontaneity. BRIGITTE BARDOT, for the symbol of the French pin-up, for ST TROPEZ, for the liberation of women, for the creature shaped by a modern Pygmalion... AND GOD CREATED B.B.

PATRICK DUPONT for the dance, French discipline between all, of course but also for its undisciplined side. Do Maurice BEJART and Roland PETIT come before NOUREEV, BARYCHNIKOV or Carolyn CARLSON?

RAN, Japanese cinema for KUROSAWA and OSHIMA, but also for SHAKESPEARE.

Women's legs for their fantasies in black stockings and high heels.... monsters of S.F, demons and wonders inspired by the worlds of LOVECRAFT, surrealist painters and the dreamlike landscapes of B.D. GAINSBOURG, the genius jack-of-all-trades for his beat, for RIMBAUD - first name Arthur -, for his "x" rhymes, for his lucid and perverse eroticism and his way of going always further in the provocation. GRACE JONES for the wild beauty, the passage from fashion to cinema, from song to photo, for her technological records ... and for her black man-eating look.

The anamorphosis and the distortions of images always present in the Azedian drawings of "FEMMES FATALES" and other "HERMAPHRODITES". SUPERMAN, of course for the SUPERMANIES...

CONAN THE BARBARIAN, the ultimate hero, for the texts of Robert HOWARD, the drawings of John BUSCEMA, the films with ARNOLD...
A thought for *A CLOCKWORK ORANGE* and *STAR WARS*. BOY GEORGE for having the nerve to be a made-up man (like many ROCKSTARS) but not wanting to wash his face anymore, and for his sweet melodies. It is a little the ZIGGY of the '80s. HARD ROCK because it's the only musical trend where the visual staging is still important with glittery costumes, leather, lizard and all the "grand guignol" paraphernalia (ALICE COOPER, WASP, MOTLEY CRÜE... LOS ANGELES bands, in general).

Hollywood glamour stars for the perfection of the icy images, the fiery kisses and the war of the tits. The femme fatales, dangerous in every way, all dressed in black with satin gloves and cigarettes, both for fashion and in period costumes, sophisticated. The charming photos for the abundance of glossy magazines.

THE SYNTHETIC IMAGES. *TRON* for allowing the comic book to flirt with the cinema. For MOEBIUS, WALT DISNEY and IBM.

JESSYE NORMAN for her unique clear and powerful voice, which gives me shivers down my back, for WAGNER, for the Opera. The disappeared civilizations for the enigmas they still pose today (Aztecs, Mayas, Egypt or Atlantis...) and for the trips they allow to dream.

Finally DAVID BOWIE for the whole of his career followed in filigree by the teenager AZED since 1972, for *ZIGGY STARDUST* and SCREAMING LORD BYRON, for all the stages, all the characters of the chameleon man.

Only one absent and of size: BAUDELAIRE... but did AZED not participate in the exhibition of the "FLOWERS OF THE MALE"?

Marseilles, 21.11.1987 by AZ

THE LILI-BITCHES

In the land of luxury Lili whores,
Lucky guitar heroes, sheltered from militia ovoid's,
Idolized a blond Eurydice, in vain.
Calling her so resolutely. But deaf, she ignored her ex.

Kicked in the squeaking of scrap metal, the thinking machine,
Ying-yang of an aesthete insect, with the most sophisticated metal
head,
Orgasmic wasn't it enough for women to upset them?
Undies at her feet, she played with him, tenderly,
Rare situation remained impassive, exhaled hints of the impossible.

Finally, in the middle of nowhere, a sophisticated princess,
Expected some mail from her;
Maeva, lascivious, attentive to outdated sophisms,
In her latex Sophie undies with devoted sapphires.

Nude in satin and red silk carpet, an incendiary brunette waits an
It girl in the exuberance of a plastic swallower, acids, rancid rubber
Never the shadows with moon masks stirred up.
Ebony Big beautiful women shake their booty for a pale beauty.

Any super-man knows it; we end up
Soon as a tiny puppet of a god with undefined sex,
Solitary, who passes over his lips from red to infinity.

SUPERMANIAC

A masquerade of exchanged promises, accomplish kissing.
Loving to relive his past, as one violates a mystery,
White Young Superman, is lying, red cloak splitting the air.
And he had so many women met, known... and then forgotten!
Yet the fleeting happiness, the moment of a clock, are gone.
Sparks of organs, white lava in the dark night.

Her white angels heels, devils in black tights,
Are some memories of sighs, smiles and hopes,
Poor memories of orgasms as if in an outlet,

Part of zephyrs, those long summer nights are full of sighs!
Yellow visions for the perverse bestialities filled the "X"
To the terrible moment of X-Factor as the fateful decision came:
Orgiac dinners are lasted an entire eternity.

Since then, if he had met poorly-mooned chicks,
He would have been a better romantic artist or a businessman
Open to passionate dreams about the stock market and politics?

Outside, would the man who walks on the moon have succumbed,
To the female experts in narcissism and body-building,
Seducing boys when others coat themselves with body-painting?

Every time! How many times, he too, had thought of
Xtc to rape this plastic beauty, this stupid half-saddle
Tuned by her exemplary lover, expert worthy of mention in the annals
Abandoned without restraint on the hot sand of the beaches
Perhaps for the only one of his looks stealing all his courage.

Ever was always there, beautiful, naked, the woman of pleasure
Offered. He had always loved her with a shadow of desire
For her unique love, always ready to confuse good and males.

And to think that this treacherous idea obsessed him,
Gee! She got drunk, and to think that she dared
One evening after a bucco-genital champagne,
Didn't she called him a... potato!!!!

VIBRATING LASER DILDO

Manhattan, laser vibrator hungry for obscenities,
At the end of each century, memory and worldliness are laid.
So confident of himself, a blue Archangel in cape and vinyl,
Too dark, help the connected wrist strap to search in her vile memories.

Undressed girls weary by time and they feel, against hers, their
Rubbed skins filled with memories of Russian television screens.
Barbarella lulled by dreams from the time she became Venus
After, from a salt statue, she was changed into a statue of a bitch.

Too cheated, she hesitated between taking revenge on metal men
Eating or plunge them, forever, into the infinity of mental suicide.
Apple big New York has a strange futuristic theatrical appearance.

Despite the looks of bitches with black gold caps
If he could, with half-closed eyes, fantasies of chains, of abhorred hope,
Carpet for her, slowly, the man with torn eyes gets tired,
Kissing her hard belly, spits out the stolen moments of passing time.

VOYOR

Voyeurism, another facet of the exhibition,
Imbearb Narcissus, you offer, for pure pleasure, your
Corrupted visions of naked girls, innocent but accomplices,
Infernal black beauties, spies of the crotch.

Octopussys'evil woman with vampire instincts, turns your mask
Upon us to become an empire knight. In allegorical dances,
Seductive baby, listen. On men, you provoke fascination!

LITTLE ASS

All the nympho-man-iac satyrs
Do likes to see the breasts of female rockstars
And they live their life hard, with an endless hope,
Many more that one last time.

In a fleeting moment, Sophia the female robot
Seem to get stuck as soon as she talk about
All perverse and sensual fantasies with some nurses.

Filled, she is proud to show her narcissism.
Only one ass could escape the stings of these ladies,
Or search the thong of their female nymphomaniac.

The shock! We're thinking about their best moments of life.

Living on the ass of her best girlfriend is a revolution.
It's the way to receive an aggression by tall female bodybuilder.

Charming Prince is shocking under a wig and satin stockings with
Kiwi fruits in his boxer, making an humanoid become heterosexual.
Eve is shocked. Ain't it with the ass that we make children?
Rare will be the moments the hero prefers to avoid these questions.

THE ARTIST AND THE BLANK PAGE

Lonely, Superman, threatened by the torments of unemployment,
Only can suffocate in the great trunk of the nightmare.
Venus in furs humiliates her beaten happy artist
Even if he hesitate between vice and virtue.

Many of his minds devoured by rats, the sweet transvestite
Excited, in vain, by paper girls dreams of castrating women
Or tortures by the high heels on his tax fantasies.
Natas will haras, with forbidden thoughts,
A naked man crushed by his hat.

But what is Superman doing in this mental torture?
Obsessed with Death, he is proud to continue
A perverse game which let him forget the blank page.
That closes the best days of his life.

THE EMPEROR OF IDEAS

Generally, fortune begins in a banal way.
Owner of a castle, Super-Cat attracts venal girls.
Dollars must not let the money curse begin
Down under penalty of knowing the invention of a sub-agent.

Even rage or despair; There won't always be a
Serene, the public man exchanged his Peugeot for a Rolls.
Superman stay in a miniature car at the fair
Proud to arrest in mid-flight a bad guy with a black soul
Reeves is proud to divide the little people into swarms of poultry,
Or Human scraps labelled behind acronyms and initials.

Ulysses rapes and veils the cameras of Atlantis' black volcano,
Deter them from going up in the air by wearing black tights.
At las, turning off social struggles to be tough won't be enough on a
Discreet yacht with softened lights for a triple erection election.

Over the height of vanity for the Emperor of Ideas,
Restore the Agile erection of an inhuman statue deformed
Ever Kicking his passions, he scattered the living forces of leather
Soldiers in an exaggeration beyond imagination.

Cool cat is in life like as a movie star. His images ignores reason.
United on the sofa, the royal couple creaks in the
Negative darkness of their prison.

Never born to reign, according to them alone,
Isis relax under the wing of an angel of good will.

Lex Luthor thought he deserved the chauvinistic colors
Inside the heart of the Gallic rooster

Nothing change when the royal distances are firmly kept.
Guys would have tried to escape the red and blue tights,
Unbelieve And his lust would have brought tears and disappointments.
Seem to be or not to be a hero, just for a day; a hit!

Embraced by the shoulder, sitting in pairs in front of their
XXL TV or standing alone upon their bed.
Completely naked from shoulders to the waist,
Every day they absorbed the images until they were disgusted.

So, one night, he wanted to measure the size of his black rocket,
Sorry to verify the old adage, written in some old grimoire.
Is love measured by the number of orgasms or just the size of his organ?
Victoria, stunned and terrified, changed her languid face
Ending the whole soul of the old politician, found himself drowned.

DREAMS IN EVE
BUTT NAKED

Whipped by the beautiful speech of the Antichrist
Hermes imagines the worst, safe from his office.
You do think the politicians are practicing the adultery.

Superman adjusts his cape to the pantyhose of his life.
His successes, his victories… Lois has never applauded him.
Over many ministers, how many evenings renouncing to
Execute their justice, in punishment,
Spying, in silence, on the innocent women of the papers.

Despite European icon with the claws of the Must de Cartier,
Although every day, your images fill our lives, America, is far away.
Nobody with a skinny fellow could accomplish
Cartoons in those hours he should have spent in weight training.
Every day, if he could have avoided speeches, meetings and libations.

I violate the secrets of paper enemies, copy of the Supermen
Naked near oracles of press bosses, transvestite ministers
Almost drunk with bad whisky. Before to sleep.

Stiff crazy girls are found of bad life.
Our citizens, stuffed with comics and blockbusters, are ruminating
Forgetting the Empire States for a Statue of Liberty
Thinking he was a newly resurrected King Kong.

Lonely are women in all this, you might say?

If necessary, their men will wear outfits in a dream crime.

For never been caught in the act of love in EVE's figue leaf,

Even if all they have to do is shut up, like girsl with a bad life!

EMMANUELLE AND THE BIG APPLE

Gorgeous lady at the gates of the desert that borders the big city,
Once upon a time, Emmanuelle dreamed, far from manly desires.
Divine carefree creature, she got aged. She had five lifting on a row.

Loving some forgotten homo-sexy, iconoclast graphic designer,
Oprah would have been so ulcerated in her sweet evening.
Vain writer filmmaker gagged by mental torture
Eleventh coitus interrupted by thoughts of secrets from his muse
Sapho's hedonist lost between alarming lovers and sadistics.

She withdraws into herself, a fœtus from a long time ago,
An adept of satin, white cotton wool cushions in the black night.
Virtue spread in the horny pages of her old grimoire
And in the reliefs of silk, sculpts her body as if by magic.

Genuine Cinderella of the Year 2030 forgets to honor old heroes.
Essential laser guitarists of the 70's offer their pedestal to Rambo.
She who thinks sophism and feminism in beloved fantasies?

Emmanuelle, would have pulled on her string to smile gently about her
X-rated movie which maybe should stay in a hidden box.
Uncle Superman, hairless, keep his head down.
Adept of the blondes with cigarettes, standing on an overboard,
Let's meditate on the psychoanalysis of Cinderella's tale!

Alone Charming Prince, emaciated, raging, guy in a tutu, dance.
Could Cinderella pick up a shoe of a Charming Prince?
Tuned In her street, excited under the reflections of the red spots,
It was before her amnesia; Now, she is looking better.

Vicky, so beautiful, so whore, so red stick on her lips spread!
I always loved her trying the shoe on men of good fortune
Thinking her ideas of obscene fantasies that only she can unveil.

In the past, it was so much better when she was twenty years old!
Energic but mute as a grave, he remains silent, a follower of secrets,
Sometimes his arms fall off. Long time ago, he was a teenager.

TESTING TEST TUBE

Alain Zirah & Herve Lechevalier

The handsome unicorn threw away its old stupid mask
Hastened to steal the test tubes of some mutant babies.
In the Good Looking Club, an evil creature with manly attributes,
Stairs at the flapping doors. Superb-Man

In silence, out of a flying saucer, a fly looking playmate fly.
Sat in their regular life including reading glasses is beyond themselves.
As beautiful tall women, they are proud to be Amazons.

From the plane filled with the most beautiful females of the creation,
A gremlin, a child's dragon, going towards a unknown destination.

To the countries where the white beautiful blonde slave
Woman trade are taking place on opened market,
On the spirit of the Vigilante Galaxy, whose mask has fallen,
Mom comes landing on the red carpet of her ideas.

As he knows that, from now on, he will not be able to have kids
Merchandised from the supermarket. He is "obsexed".

SUPERMAN IN SUBWAY

Prometheus, in the evenings in the subway,
Recently as you can even see comic book supermarkets letting some
Eclectic Adonis themselves be tempted gay.
Terrible! The mores have changed a lot!
To top it off, they're grabbing the soft buttocks of former super-heroins.

You'd never know what the straight vigilante has aged so well.
Where could he still play at his age? In a sandbox?
He can't stand that time erases all those beautiful invisible scars
On Ulysses faces of the suburbs making impressive grimaces.

Rebellious, he claims some metal studded leather fantasies
Evicted, without imagining his head turning into a pincushion.

So sexy, he lets himself be done, confusing being tortured for pleasure.
And women, made so beautiful, due to their strong personalities,
Rarely trying to remain the image of a memory.
Even if Superman is a philosopher; to be, being or has been.

To die fallen is worse than to become a drunkard!
With passionate embraces, fatal relationships,
Oldest women have always known how to play with men.

By female dolls who play the hook, baited, like the most common fish,
Reduced to plastic maid and human ashtray
And his phone, an absent subscriber, is dying for no reason.
The super-old-man becomes an obedient toy, that asshole!

WHAT IS THERE UNDER THE KILT?

When a blue man flies, as a stupid robot on his beautiful iron horse
Or swim because he doesn't fear, what a big kohoona will dock him?

Under the watchful eye of a knight in a kilt made of Scottish thread,
Like Frankenstein writing the Flowers of Evil,
Doctor Moreau creates great dolls form the bodies of his victims
That he hides in the crazy forest of his island.

He has ember eyes; he abuses the fatal brunettes and blonde girls.
Aphrodisiac syringe, whenever you wish, you spit!

The first female giant, without her knowledge victorious,
But goes to crush under her foot some human ants
Even with a prestigious past.
A delay for the deadline. Bitch! Bitch!

But would she talk to ants with a prestigious past?
Remind us how pods are transformed into creatures.
Everywhere we must not forget the "body snatchers".
Aware of the tragedy that gnaws at humanity, in secret,
She sketches a smile. Will she stay immobile?

Too giant in black leather, another Mona Lisa have a fragile heart.
Lolita, Helen of Troy, Antigone of Hollywood or Phaedra,
Odd By juggling with the greenish eggs of a fearsome alien,
Victorious, more than running, women's legs have better things to do!
Entering in The Crazy Horse, he would like to seduce her. And the
Rich man, owner of a football team has so much to tell !

LASER VIBRATIONS

A vibratory laser! Finally a signal in space!
Nose to the wind, the red cape swings towards the distress call.
Outside the long-haired countryside, the hero does not wear a braid.

Tempted by adventure, a vigilante with white hair, sex and pure
Heart is trying to tear apart the Frankenstein apprentice of the future
Escape attracted by a monstrous creature with big noce.
Really feeding exclusively fresh blood to its boiling offspring.
Slave to the escalation of half-naked girls, he measures his progress.
Looking for who may need help; no escape!
A king is a homunculus of operetta, making the Kong,
Vigilante waiting on a chair of his ovoid tower,
Even with his virtue for a delirious one with a slightly hard look.

Libertine Miss Ingenuous and Latin Trollop disturb bliss
Invented by a Jeckyll which gets excited on sophisticated puppets
Clearly obsessed with their high infidelity channel in the evening.
Kinky drunk with covet infernal powers and dark forces
She dyes her hair pink, this young neo whore, wearing panties...
Hand in hand they convolve in their dance of impure girls.
Everyone could realizes that they are only humanoid toys.

Rarely stripped, the blonde woman doesn't wear a skirt!

Creeping from legs sheathed with polished bayonet heels.
Unchained in his pedestal cage, in a too warm sky, cheating the
Nudity of Time Goddess with fishnet and high heels,
Never forgetting appearances, the Keeper of the Great Secret swoons.
It's so hot! Admiring, the lonely God practices fantasy.

THE MIRACLE MAKER

Dante's Hell, the antechamber of horror
Reveals his strange secrets and darkest thoughts.
Eva and Adam, the good and the male
And illusory monsters in a face-to-face buttock,
Makes the World ridiculous with monstrous illusions.

Odds demons with dead bodies born, creatures with atrophied breasts,
Fuck metal hybrids with the faces of beautiful women.
Plastic robots that look like almost women,
Android dream creatures and rather swollen dolls.

My souvenirs have escaped from the archipelago of my memory.
Eternal in the chaos, which precedes the primal writing,
Long time ago, he had done some tests, the Miracle Maker.
Awesome Eve changed into Cinderella, forgetting her first life.

So that, the captivated blonde, the hot brunette and the scarlet redhead
Immerse themselves in the texts and dream in front of the images.
Some will pee on this work with large jets of printer's ink
To think to success as other wash their feet in the basin of indifference.

Evently, there were so many sumo factories, we had to abort,
Running with so many self-censored ideas and suicidal thoughts.
Seriously, for them, other people's dream they are golden boys.

Inside the matrix, everything is done for the love of women.
Not only yellow graces, Asian blacks and other beautiful sleepers,
Lascivious, all those girls warm up the glossy paper's goddesses.

Eating their tits, they analyze their delusions and paranoia of their
Slaves. To persecute other ideas, they reject their seriousness.
But after all, is life really have serious reasons to be?
Or is there something else? In another universe, where
Sexy Cenobites play with your psycho-sexual fantasies.

LILLIPUTIAN
STAKHANOVIST

She has a crush on the heroes in spandex,
He helped her to catch the thief red handed in her purse.
In the light of a lunar desert, a smiling Lilliputian
Too happy to trade her noodles against donuts,

Soon, farther, a large hairy male, depilated chest,
Make mercy to an icy blonde sucker with merciless eyes.
Our Emmanuelle, half-naked snake,
Kneeled. He tries to attract her, but she offers back her services to him.
Every time you pay and you can to warm her up.

Richard, why choose between the useful and the pleasant?
Irina wearing "seven leagues boots", knows how to steal from men
Leaving their love carved in the marble.
Obviously, she learned how to take them, to mark them with her nails
Vicious, scratching their backs, to make them reach the seven skies.
Ending up having other desires than to satisfy the perverse manipulator.
And she knows how to be respected as a woman.

Poor soldier, sex stakhanovist, Half-naked under her cape,
Only Alone, she want to have fun with her hand.
One night, to make love in a car, to climax under a porch.
Thinking some unusual fantasies; having sex on top of a Porsche.

Cinderella, as a modern whore is looking for a shoe that fits her.

Heroic, the cheap Superman, helped by strangers without any faces

Or any hair on his skull remain stunned.

On the way to go down on her, with caresses,

A cunnilingus expert, with forked tongue and a bitch tongue,

A wanton brunette offers one of her students a whole night of promises,

Savage and pure, until she open up the doors of unknown domains.

MOONLIGHT JIG

Insensitive, the Queen of Stone frozen in a statue of libertine freedom,
Wears out, with languor, his hair scattered.
And in a battle of titans, greases turn heads
Nobles Venus in their splendid cars eager for rabbit's eyes.
Too much adult toys. All night long, he'll sucks licorice.

Feet of Miss slips discovers foreign languages
And teaches the unknown soldier a new way to get off on his feet.
Creepy girl has been drinking and talking alone all evening.
Electrified by the not very clear daughter-in-law of a star, the stupid
Superman dances the jig with a guy in the moonlight.

Invisible boots lifting their rider, light as a feather.
To the victory, the fugitive opens his trap of animal skins memories,
Too quickly! Because life today is like a run.
Ivory under the gigantic ebony statue, drunk dominatrix,
Nightingale looks like a diva, she plays with a smile,
Gagging his mouth, with the delicacy of her singing voice.

FORBIDDEN SENSATIONS

By knocking the handle of the heavy door of his last vision,
A necrotic hand, without any word, drops a reduced head of a dwarf.
Twisting a poor victim, a tall zombie of the old strong sex
Makes a middle finger salute to the blue lightning hulk,
At the feet of the weaker sex, prohibited by so many taboos.

Nono, the voiceless robot stays at the end, sour,
Arse-licker escaping the advances of a naked delusional woman,
Licking her life, stroking her little one.

With a sacred dance stepped damn wise, fan of girls of little virtue,
Always exaggerating exuberance, with a look to improbable turtle,
Young VIP in tuxedo and Givenchy incite the indecent exhibition of
Salome from the salons where she has set her seven sails.

Silent, forbidden monks, barely escaped from the Forbidden City.
Under her kryptonite high heel shoes
Cool Superman, his back nailed to the ground, like
Kafka a woodlouse on a needle living its last ups and downs.

Pretty vacant hero waits for help from a naked stranger.
Upstairs, she offers her butt, deaf to incongruous calls.

Such a bitch with the appearance of a boy,
She ignores her ex-boyfriend and falls asleep in the dark.
You, buried in your forbidden intimacy will finish greedy for eels.

ALL ITS FORBIDDEN SENSES

At the feet of the weaker sex,
Rudely knocking the handle of the heavy door to bash the bishop,
Robin shakes his necrotic hand without a word for a female celebrity,
Oracle, the red hair, drops the reduced head of a seduced dwarf,
With some sacred dance steps,

Prohibited by so many taboos,
Rob the robot with no voice suddenly dances, sour by his last visions.
Escaping the advances of a naked delusional woman.
Followers of small virtuous cities, without a look for improbable turtles,
Exaggerating their exuberance, he moves his hands like a white flag.
Ready to shake her booty with sensuality, without a pity for her victim.
She strokes the useless nuts of her little zombie damn wise.

To greedy monks, barely escaped from a Forbidden City,
Our VIP masters, in tuxedo and Givenchy, invite in indecent exhibition.

Salome from the wet salons has set sail.
Under her ultra-fashioned sexy kryptonite pumps
Cool Superman, his back nailed to the ground, alike
Kafka, a bug pierced on a needle.

Waiting for the help from a naked stranger.
Ô awesome deaf, she offers you her butt,
Man-eater tom-boy, snake lover greedy for
Eels buried in her forbidden intimacy,
Naomi ignores her ex-boy toy and falls asleep in the back seat.

*

INTO THE NEURAL BUBBLE

In his sponge bubble with neurons that fattened,
Still, a furry Cinderella loses her glass shoe.
Go beautiful women and dance, insensitive to
Oiled bodybuilded men. Too eager to fight small green monsters,

Dark Superman has found his soul mate. He "kryptobites" her.
Lost enthusiast voyeuristic, under the gaze of a meteorite accomplice.
Off the wall, he practices the discovery of incongruous objects,
Victim of a blond ephebe in shining armor, who tempted him.

If satyrs always pulled themselves towards other horizons,
No attraction except lured by the bad graces of a future baritone,
Going so far from her, the man with sharp eyebrows,
Pumped until he became deaf to the sounds of his daughter-in-law,
Undies addict, the indelicate thongs lover, gored, fresh out of his tent,
Sexually corruptible give a last shot with the bad boys.

Skillful lucky people would jump to the ceiling.
In a wink, he authorized his son-in-law to pass the oil
Eye-popping on the sumptuous skin of bodybuilded women.
Scratch when we got out of line and secretly offers one last spurt.

THE FINAL EXPLOSION

Like the chaos that follows the final explosion
I talk to The Lord who chains up Time in order to complete his work.

Cuckold, deaf to the calls from the weaker sex
Known, the futuristic angel leaves the world to
Meditate. His real place is somewhere else and he knows that.

You Horned Zebu, racing like crazy, Adam will wake up Eve.
Las, despite the cries of the last dying God, he seizes her.
If you could imagine that life doesn't make no sense!

Finally, he's searching fireworks in the sky, in vain.
Earth passengers, why should Death make any sense?

USA FOREVER

L.A. 2003

The dragon in peaceful life transcend a delicate symphony While the glimmering fragrance spice tells her a talk of pleasure, The happy beauty promised love and dreams.

Two bared souls adore explosions of joy.
The goddess face sweats like in a crazy ecstasy.
She shouts to the gorgeous phoenix: « Possess me, you sensual god! »

Why do precious moments create adrenaline lights?
A sensuous emotion crisps under the crimson flood valley And he collapses, who sang a minor mammal smell show!

Dark become clear to the destiny
While those orange clouds dive deeply to the mystery zenith We felt in the true abyss as the silent song flows without reason.

The two sensuous bodies go bathe naked in the merry garden In the paradise, the birth of a tranquil woman promise sorrow But the blue snake whispers caress and pleasure.

The shadow eats the divine blood enemy of love
And the mirror ship of passion fly between the clouds.
So they wake up relaxed in the deep purple harmony of happiness.

Guess who wants the pictures of perfumed heart eternity! When the white cat runs under the angel's window,
The crimson happy beauty wishes the true meaning of life.

She knows that she can't stop running too,
But she dreams of translucent rose bridge with lazy Life is so wild and
love shout its deeply symphony.

The golden angel kisses the majestic breast of the silver heaven.
Darker mysteries become so clear and deep
When the friendly phoenix brings the gift of eternity.

THE GOLDEN WINGS

Imagine the lost savage garden in wild winter land. Imagine the divine garden in the lost land
Where god and goddess never imagined man and woman…

The softly goddess likes a hard desire for ecstasy.
She dreams of love and translucent rose bridge with lazy. The happy beauty promised love and dreams.

She shouts to the gorgeous phoenix: « Possess me, you sensual god! »
And, for her, he dances between the clouds in perfect harmony.
Then he jumps on the divine orange body, hot like a volcano.

The two bared souls adore all their skins in explosions of joy.
The goddess face sweat like in a crazy energy. Her breast peep out.
And, with all his energy, the gentle hero build a translucent rose bridge.

His crazy lazy face sweat a sensuous black emotion 'Cause he knows that dark mystery excite the lazy destiny
and the precious moments create shimmering daylight in his heart.

After love, she relaxes her lethargic celestial thighs with passion. The phoenix lover looks her naked body and legs; he smiles.
The happy beauty change her purple tears in bright orange juice.

The paradise promises serenity for the lovers
And the warm perfume of temple's fountains guide the lovers To peaceful symphony.

She kisses her god and he gives her explosion of joy, deeply.

Then, time passes by, and the power of love calms the ecstasy of volcano. He loves her eyes, her soul, her legs, so it's time to ask her hand.

But in this promised land, there is no mayor nor notary. They are alone… So, it's time, now, for man, woman and fruits to appear, the snake says…

THE BROKEN WINGS

Imagine the lost savage garden in wild winter land. The softly goddess
likes a hard desire for ecstasy
And the gentle hero build a translucent rose bridge with all his energy.

His crazy lazy face sweat a sensuous emotion
'Cause he knows that dark mystery excites the lazy destiny
and the precious moments create shimmering daylight in his heart.

She sweeps venom from praise to discover the friendly phoenix. The
happy beauty promises purple eternity diving in bright orange And
she relaxes her lethargic celestial thighs with passion.

The paradise may promise sorrow or serenity for the lovers
But the fountains of temple will guide them in a peaceful symphony.
She kisses her god and he gives her explosion of joy, deeply.

Then, time passes by, time after time, in the white silver heaven.
The golden jewels of their hearts rust and flow in a silver screen
Thereafter the rain crashed on the azure mirror of the fateful doom.

THE TERRIFIC GIRL WITH OPENED EYES

Elle is a gorgeous woman with a golden helmet and sparkling eyes.
She lives in L.A., in a Provencal way, sometime with a white cat.
With her car and her phones, she wants to rule the world.

Elle is a perfect blonde with a hidden smile.
The death knocked to her door but she refused to open. Unfortunately,
friends sometimes let their open house.

One day, when Elle came back to her ordered life
A man was sitting. He enters without apologize; it's crazy, isn't it?
Who's this crazy lazy boy without car in such a huge city?

He uses candle lights to see her skin, her eyes and her soul But she
doesn't want to exhibit her inside without permission.
She wants the man to be a fly, but the dragonfly changes in butterfly.

The contact with the two big souls makes sparkles of positive energy
And the woman explodes like a living old volcano
With fireworks in her eyes; he smiles.

He takes his third eye and Elle shows her eyes, her body and her soul.
The terrific girl has just discovered the skeleton in closet of his life.
Then, she brings the best breakfast to a new happy life.

Alain Zirah for Elle Travis-Peterson - Santa Monica/Los Angeles
– 03/10/2003

GUESS WHO...

Guess who wants the pictures of perfumed heart eternity! When the white cat runs under the angel's window,
The crimson happy beauty wishes the true sense of life.

She knows that she can't stop running too,
But she dreams of translucent rose bridge with lazy Life is so wild and love shout its deeply symphony.

The golden angel kiss the majestic breast of the silver heaven. Darker mysteries become so clear and deep
When the friendly phoenix brings the gift of eternity.

Beware of the vampires' dollars' suckers carrying their bliss dreams
And scream false fire in black water of bloody shadows!
The warm perfume of temple's fountains build serenity.

Swansongs and dragonflies dance under the rain While the mountains swallow the stardust of heaven.

The dark become mystery and excite the destiny. Skins and souls are the only energy in their eyes.

EDEN ROCK

The precious moments create light in the day And sensuous emotions pervade in peace.
So, the bodies float in the silver white heaven.

Spring drinks the colored blood of death. Imagine the divine garden in the lost land
Where god and goddess never imagined man and woman…

A tender rainbow slips in a delicate symphony of colors While a majestic golden angel raise in the cloudy rain. The delirious power of love calms the ecstasy of volcano.

The crimson goddess change in a precious green snake And the cold burner king of gods shines his precious jewels
The strength of a man and the spice perfume of his first lady.

Rain crashes the mirror of the azure fate
As their golden jewel hearts beat in explosion of joy.

VARNISH ON MY SOUL

I put varnish on my soul
Some gloss on my lips and on my toes, You came and go with my grinning soul.

My body's wicked, if you go...
You terrified my love, step on my loneliness. I whip your pride, my lovely priestess.
With arrogance, I tear your wrong feelings I want you come back to me.

Black in white. Sweet and savage African beauty. Skin oiled with perfume and coconut milk.
Black skin in white cotton from duty
Free. How could I forget, hand in hand, the silk Of your lips on my body.

And darkness of your blood. 'Cause, angel, so dark is your blood.

You can change the colors of your hair.
Put amethyst on your eyes, black around your lips. When the music flows, you move your hips.

Don't change your older minds And can't escape to love
The man still standing in your shadow.

We've been so far away
But love forever still beating, someday,

In sharp trousers moving on the dancefloor.

Don't change your older minds Babe, you can't escape your love
With the man still standing in your shadow.

I collect your body inside my lens To print your smile under my eyelid.

Don't fear your love
With ivory of my skin, I'll just shine your life. Babe, you can't escape your love
Just stay forever in my life.

And I'll still be the man that you always love With ivory of my skin, I'll just shine your life,
And I'll stay the man still standing in your shadow.

Marseilles –The Paradox – 03/09/2007

KENNY SINGS THE BLUES

Sweet beauty from Ethiopia and America,
You sing the bluesy moment of your childhood And call all the children of the holly hoods
To sing, with you, the rescue of the Earth.

As the African queen of a men company, You whisper life, hope and money When I prefer you just sing with honey.

Beautiful lady from San Francisco, The war, why can't we stop it?
The love of life, how can we keep it?

I met you and you became my never-ending sister Who stand under a lucky star.
A six-spiked star, to celebrate you as a music star.

In your foreign language, you drink red wine
Of universal community and ask, with your little voice, Mum and Dad, where are you now?

And, for your new brother, you must shine brightly as a pop star To meet then again, later, far away in the stars.

Alain Zirah for Kenny Joyce in Paris 09.09.09

THE UNIVERSAL QUEEN

Beautiful eyed lady from San Francisco,
I paint your all body with the pure oil of my soul.

Charismatic Lady who want to change the world
As a crossover from Indian Jones and a Black Panther You spoke so much about the love of your father
And I reply about Black Kat Ladies around the world.

Don't change your mind, Ô sweet mystic eyes.
You told me how you have been the first black beauty queen And how I became the servant in the shadow of your soul.

You celebrate the victory of your "Venus Mercenaries" Who conquest photographers' eyes
To become icons of fashion on glossy paper.

Please accept to be a Black Kat Lady
For showing to the world the entire African spirit And let the beauty of your soul stay in luxurious spa.

You may turn your dead hairs from yellow to red And open doors for Black Tigresses Ladies
Just to tell in the ever-cycling show of life
"Life has been good, even before I woke up as an icon."

Alain Zirah for Shaun Ollison in Paris 09.10.09

FASCINATION

Why are women so fascinating ?
I could stay alone, reading magazines In Central Station, drinking diet coke

But women are like dangerous red ants Or spiders. They just keep on walking And their legs pick my eyes.

It's warmy summer. Women are hot And quite rude. Long and naked legs Danse on the cleaned floor.

Feet leaved their leather jail. Feet are free. They play with colors in plastic
Or white, black or brown classy sandals.

I just want to keep my attention on my book, But women shake boobs and booty
Just under my nose and my victimed eyes.

The curves of the smooth women ass Are still fascinating me
As is fascinated the white skin Under the feet of the black ladies.

SUMMARY